*Leonard of Pisa and
the New Mathematics
of the Middle Ages*

LEONARD OF PISA
AND THE
NEW MATHEMATICS
OF THE
MIDDLE AGES

By Joseph and Frances Gies
Illustrated by Enrico Arno

Reprinted by
New Classics Library
a division of
Elliott Wave International, Inc.
Post Office Box 1618
Gainesville, GA 30503
With special permission from
HarperCollins Publishers

ACKNOWLEDGMENTS

In writing this book the authors profited from the assistance of Professor David Herlihy of the University of Wisconsin, author of *Pisa in the Early Renaissance*, and Professor Marguerite Dunton of Sacramento State College, coauthor (with her husband, Professor R.E. Grimm) of a forthcoming translation of Leonard Fibonacci's works, never before translated into English.

The book was researched in four libraries: the Sterling Library of Yale University; the Newberry Library, Chicago; the John Crerar Library of the Illinois Institute of Technology; and the Northwestern University Library.

Designed by Judie Mills

Manufactured in the United States of America

ISBN: 0-317578-49-9

Library of Congress Catalog Card Number: 71-81952

To our son Charles,
and all the other new mathematicians

A NOTE
ON LEONARD'S NAME

Leonard's name (in Latin) appears in the *incipites* (titles) of manuscripts of his books in three different ways:

Leonardus Pisanus (Leonard the Pisan).

Leonardus filius Bonaccii (Leonard Fibonacci), Fibonacci apparently being the family's surname in Italian. Leonard's father is mentioned in a contemporary document as "Gulielmus" (William).

Leonardus Bigollus. "Bigollo" in Tuscan dialect is difficult to translate, but an equivalent might be "absent-minded."

CONTENTS

I

THE WORLD OF
LEONARD FIBONACCI

No visitor to Italy would miss the city on the northwest
coast where a 185-foot tower of white marble leans sev-
enteen feet from the perpendicular. But after climbing
and photographing the Leaning Tower and admiring
the cathedral, baptistery, and Campo Santo, tourists find
little else to see in Pisa. Few visit a less spectacular
monument on the other side of the Arno: the statue
of a man. This statue is unusual in that its subject is
neither a general nor a statesman, but a mathematician.

A contemporary of the architect who began the Leaning Tower, Leonard Fibonacci made a contribution to
our civilization immeasurably more important than a
bell tower, leaning or straight. The greatest Western
mathematician of the Middle Ages, he was largely
responsible for introducing into Europe an indispensable tool for mathematical progress, and thereby made
a major contribution to the development of modern
mathematics, with all its momentous consequences to
science and technology. This tool, imported into Italy

from Arab North Africa, was Hindu-Arabic notation, including the critically important zero.

As with most medieval personages, we do not know many details of Leonard's life—little beyond what he set down on a single page of his best-known work, the *Liber abaci (Book of Calculation)*. But we know that he was a man of genius, and that he was a citizen of a remarkable republic—the city-state of Pisa. Though it was a small town by today's standards, with a population of only about ten thousand, twelfth-century Pisa played a major role in the "Commercial Revolution" of the twelfth and thirteenth centuries. This revolution transformed Europe and paved the way for the industrial, scientific, and technological revolutions of the modern era.

Leonard's own lifework, the introduction, interpretation, and exposition of a new system of numerals, had obvious relevance for an expanding, business-oriented society. Even more important was the long-range impact of the new numerals which, like so many elements in the cultural revival that accompanied the Commercial Revolution, were transmitted to Western Europe by the Arabs from an older civilization, in this case that of India. Leonard himself always referred to the new numbers as "Hindu," though later writers labeled them "Hindu-Arabic" or "Arabic."

Leonard of Pisa appeared on the scene some two centuries after the end of the economic and cultural slowdown which we call the Dark Ages—the period of barbarian invasion and disruption from the fifth to tenth centuries. Europe had already begun to awaken from stagnation. Improvements in farming techniques made it possible to raise more food, and this increase in production contributed to a population explosion which in its turn created a rapidly growing demand for goods and services of all kinds. An expansion of commerce was in progress which surpassed anything that had gone before.

Though most of this commerce was local—farmers bringing their produce to market in the city, and buying products from city craftsmen—a small but highly important part was long-distance and international. Poor roads handicapped land transport; it was much cheaper, and usually faster, to carry goods by sea. As in ancient times, the Mediterranean became a broad avenue linking regions which represented many different religions, political entities, and cultures. Most of the civilization of the Western half of the world clustered around its shores.

The other half of the world, the Far East, was remote but by no means inaccessible. Cargoes were brought by ship from India and Ceylon to the head of the Persian Gulf, thence up the Tigris to Baghdad or Mosul and overland to Syria, or to the Red Sea ports of Egypt and by caravan—camel or donkey—to the Nile. The most important commodity carried was spices. These included not only condiments for seasoning and preserving food, but medicines, ointments, cosmetics, dyes, tanning agents, and materials used in alchemy. Given the small capacity of medieval ships, the compactness of spices made them extraordinarily valuable cargoes. A shipload—perhaps a hundred tons—of pepper might in terms of modern U.S. currency be worth $250,000. In return for the saffron, cinnamon, pepper, and other exotic seeds, leaves, and barks which they obtained from the Arabs in the ports of the eastern Mediterranean, European merchants traded fine wool cloth, timber, iron, and other metals. European merchandise was bulkier, but traveled a shorter distance to reach the Arab market places.

Nearly all the cargoes, going and coming, were transported in the ships of a dozen European cities. Most of these cities were Italian. Three in particular dominated commerce: Venice, at the head of the Adriatic, on the northeast shoulder of Italy; Genoa, on the west coast; and Pisa, south of Genoa.

"Genoa is surrounded by walls, it submits to no king, but has magistrates chosen by the vote of the citizens to govern it," marveled Benjamin of Tudela, a Spanish Jew who passed through Italy on his way to the Holy Land in 1160. Genoa, Pisa, and Venice were notable anomalies in twelfth-century Europe, which was mostly ruled by kings, emperors, counts, and bishops. The greater part of Italy was subject to the German emperor, the king of Sicily, or the pope. But these three cities and a few others such as Milan and Florence were "communes"—virtually independent republics, sovereign within their own strong walls and over the surrounding countryside, which supplied them with food and raw materials.

The Italian cities led Europe not only in the commercial revival but in everything else. In Bologna, seventy miles northeast of Pisa, a band of students had organized a new kind of institution which they called a "university," and were busy rediscovering the valuable code of Roman law. In Salerno, to the south, men from many countries were studying at the world's first medical school. In Pisa and her sister cities, great architectural monuments were under construction. The workshops of the builders amounted to so many little engineering schools, training masons, sculptors, and architects. Throughout Italy scholars were at work translating the works of Euclid, Apollonius, Archimedes, Aristotle, and Galen from Greek or Arabic.

On the battlefield too the Italian city republics were redoubtable, as the Emperor Frederick Barbarossa learned in 1176 when the men of Milan and neighboring cities gave his army of German knights a beating at the Battle of Legnano. They were even more formidable at sea, their long slender galleys raiding and fighting the length and breadth of the Mediterranean. Venetian fleets conquered the Balkan coast across the Adriatic and drove the Muslims from parts of southern Italy. In 1016 Pisa and Genoa wrested Sardinia from the Muslims, and in 1035 sacked the rich North African city of Bône. In 1087, with contingents from Amalfi and troops furnished by the pope, they carried out a massive raid on the Muslim stronghold of Mahdia in North Africa. Pisan fleets also raided Palermo, the capital of Muslim Sicily, and Majorca, in the Balearic Islands. In the

1090s Genoese and Pisan ships powerfully seconded the vast military-naval expedition known to history as the First Crusade. From it they came away not only loaded with booty, but even more important, armed with valuable trading privileges in the Syrian ports.

The sea gate of Pisa bore a proud inscription:

By the noble citizens this is called the Golden Gate.
See in this city which is wont to strike the neck of the
  wicked
The greatest glory of the empire . . .
Terrible was the woe of the Balearic,
When she with conquered Iviza felt the power of Pisa,
Eleven hundred and fifteen years after the Virgin con-
  ceived God . . .
Love justice, ye rulers of the earth!

By mid–twelfth century Pisa had colonies, port privileges, or consular establishments throughout the Mediterranean. Pisan merchant-adventurers competed with Venetians and Greeks at Constantinople, and on the Sea of Azov. Like the other Italians, the Pisans had no scruples about doing business with the Muslims. A large part of their commerce, if not the bulk of it, was with the vast Muslim community which stretched in a crescent from Persia (Iran) around the entire eastern and southern shores of the Mediterranean to southern Spain. Flourishing cities dotted the crescent: Baghdad, Damascus, Alexandria, Tunis, Bugia (Bougie), Algiers, Granada, Cordova, and many more. Some were ancient towns conquered by the followers of Muhammad; some were recently founded.

Though Islam was subdivided into many principalities whose population ranged through a broad spectrum from Turks to Berbers, it formed a surprisingly homogeneous whole, thanks to the common religion and the common culture. This culture, like the religion, was Arabic. When Alp Arslan, the Turkish sultan of Roum, commissioned the Persian mathematician-poet Omar Khayyám to write a treatise on algebra, Omar wrote it in Arabic, for the same reason that Leonard of Pisa wrote his *Liber abaci* in Latin. Arabic was the language universally understood by the educated class in the Islamic half of the Mediterranean world, as Latin was that universally understood by the educated class in the European half.

Despite crusades, wars, and piracy, Christian Europe and Islam were involved in many peaceful and productive exchanges. Most of this contact was commercial, maintained by the seafaring businessmen of Pisa and her sister Italian cities. If ignorant knights and barons regarded Muslims solely as enemies to fight and kill, scholars as well as businessmen saw them as people from whom much could be learned.

II

PISA

Leonard Fibonacci was born in the eighth decade of the twelfth century, no one knows exactly when. His father was a Pisan business and government official, a representative of the new class produced by the Commercial Revolution.

Biographies were rare in the Middle Ages, even for kings and popes, portraits even rarer. There are no contemporary pictures of Leonard. We do know, however, how people dressed in the late twelfth and early thirteenth centuries, and we can imagine him as a young man, in a linen or woolen tunic, a sort of long shirt reaching not quite to his knees; over it a short fur-lined coat, and, for outdoor wear, an overcoat wrapped around the body and fastened at the right shoulder with a buckle; on his head a hood, or perhaps a soft cap. Since his family was well-to-do, he probably wore undergarments of linen. His legs would be encased in long tight-fitting hose, a combination of stockings and trousers. His shoes were of soft leather. Men as well as women wore bright colors, so Leonard's costume was a combination of scarlet and blue, or perhaps green and yellow.

Leonard's family probably lived in the characteristic house of Pisans: a tower. A shaft of brick or stone, rising three or more stories, the tower was either the principal feature of a Pisan house or the entire house. Often a wooden balcony projected over the street; sometimes this was the entranceway, with wooden stairs to the street. Sometimes the entrance was on the ground floor, and the stairs were inside; access to upper floors was usually by a ladder.

Windows were narrow and few; the tower in fact was a fortress as well as a dwelling and shop. Partitions were of wood. The ground floor might serve as shop or counting room, or for storing barrels of oil and wine, tools, and supplies. The second floor usually contained the hall or solar, the center of family life, and perhaps a bedroom. Kitchens were often on upper floors, so that smoke could escape easily. Unless the family was very wealthy, there were no indoor toilet facilities. Only a few houses fronting on the river had sewage disposal. Most of the others did not even have cesspools. Water had to be brought in pails from the well or fountain to be stored in stone tanks in the kitchen; a few wealthy and well-located houses had it piped from the Arno.

Pisa, an important port in Roman times, had continued to operate as a maritime center during the Dark Ages; but in the past two centuries the city had burst the old confines, and now towers rose to the east and west of the ancient Roman enclosure, and to the south, across the Arno. Benjamin of Tudela claimed that there were "almost ten thousand" towers—a medieval exaggeration which he may have derived from the patriotic boasts of Pisan citizens. "Each house has its own, for protection against quarrels which may arise," he wrote. City life was the reverse of tranquil. Family feuds and factional conflicts erupted repeatedly. No citizen felt secure unless he could take refuge in his own tower. Besides, the possession of such a petty castle conferred status. Sometimes a cluster of towers belonging to several branches of a single great family were linked by timber bridges high above the street. During feuds, tower doors were barricaded, arrows flew from the narrow windows, and boiling water and pitch rained from the balconies on the assailants below.

In Leonard's boyhood a dispute broke out among some of the leading families over the question of rebuilding Pisa's only bridge over the Arno, after a flood. Rebuilding was costly, and the town government, like governments in all ages, was short of funds. The Gualandi family, who lived near the bridge, and some other families allied with them, offered to undertake the project at their own expense. But a rival party, headed by the Albizzoni family, objected. The Gualandi, they said, would be in a position to control traffic both on and under the bridge, and even on the river banks. Fighting broke out, the Albizzoni attacked the Gualandi with flame and sword, destroying one of their towers and finally forcing a settlement under which the city government agreed to take over the rebuilding.

The bridge in question spanned the heart of Pisa's busy waterfront. Leonard must have spent many hours here on the Piazza San Niccola watching ships load and unload along the river wharves. Eight miles inland from the river mouth, the harbor had silted since Roman times, and in dry seasons was often too shallow for ships to ascend. Large vessels used Pisa's auxiliary harbor, the Porto Pisano, several miles south along the seacoast. Despite this, Pisa's location astride the Arno, the river road from inland Tuscany to the sea, sufficed to make her the leading city of the region. The enterprise of her merchants and sailors had exploited her natural advantages to place her in the forefront of international commerce.

Broad-beamed sailing ships, slim, oared galleys, heavy seagoing barges, pole-propelled river flatboats, vessels of all types brought cargoes from overseas as well as from inland. Leonard probably saw longshoremen unload sacks of grain from the Maremma, south of Pisa, salt from the island of Sardinia, bales of squirrel skins from Sicily, goatskins from North Africa, ermine from far-off Hungary. Certain ships had large doors in their sterns which opened to allow horses from Provence to be led ashore. The most valuable cargoes were alum, for Pisa's leather industry, dyes to be sold to textile manufacturers of Italy and northwest Europe, and most precious of all, the spices of the Far East. Sacks of grain and barrels of wine were transferred from ship to barge for

the voyage up the Arno to Florence. Barrels of wine and oil, bales of hemp and flax, bars of iron and silver were loaded on outgoing ships.

All this commercial activity called for records, and Leonard may have looked on while scribes and stewards prepared ships' manifests, listing the items in a cargo and their prices, in *librae* (pounds), *solidi,* and *denarii* —the universal medieval money system, preserved in modern times in the British pounds, shillings, and pence. Twelve *denarii* (pennies) made a *solidus* (shilling), and twenty *solidi* a *libra* (pound). The scribe wrote down his figures in Roman numerals, in long columns, using an abacus for the actual operation of adding, and putting down the subtotals from each page of the manifest on a final page at the end. This method of operating may have struck the boy, with his interest in arithmetic, as clumsy.

As he made his way about the city, Leonard must have seen gangs at work on the new city wall. The expanding town had outgrown its old ramparts, and at about the time of Leonard's birth the new fortifications were begun. Lofty, thick, with a parapet along the crest and flanking towers at intervals, the walls were dressed-stone shell enclosing a core of rock rubble.

The powerful walls looked both landward and seaward. Pisa had enemies in both directions, in the Muslim world and among rival Italian cities, especially Genoa. The intermittent warfare of the Italian cities gradually fused into the larger struggle between the Holy Roman (actually German) emperor and the pope.

Supporters of the empire were known as Ghibellines, those of the pope as Guelfs. Cities contained representatives of both parties, and often changed sides with changes of government, but Pisa was generally Ghibelline.

Despite her tradition of loyalty to the emperor, Pisa was in the process of establishing her independence during the eleventh century. Originally the city was part of the march of Tuscany, ruled by a marquis who owed allegiance to the emperor. The marquis's representative in Pisa was called the viscount, or vice-count. But as time passed the viscounts succeeded in keeping their office within their own family, thereby converting a political office into a hereditary fief. They took the name of the office as their family name, and for a time Pisa was ruled by the Visconti family, whose towers dominated the Mezzo or central quarter of the town. But in the twelfth century other families grew powerful enough to challenge the Visconti.

Besides the Gualandi and Albizzoni, who had fought over the rebuilding of the Arno bridge, there was the Gherardesca family, which built its own footbridge to connect its palace in the Kinsica quarter on the left bank of the river with the square where the government buildings stood. Many of these "first families" of Pisa had their palaces near the river, with steps leading down to their private wharfs.

The wealthy families had varying origins. Some were descended from shipowners and privateers who took part in the naval triumphs of the eleventh century;

some were upstarts who had only recently come to the city; some were from the feudal countryside, and still had property and roots there.

Men from these families filled most of the offices of the town government, serving as consuls and senators of the commune of Pisa. Their incessant wrangling made government so difficult that by popular decision a city manager called a *podestà* was finally appointed. The *podestà* served for one year and then had to wait for his pay until a special committee investigated his administration. Pisa's first *podestà* was a Gherardesca, but in time of exceptional stress the *podestà* was imported from outside to ensure his neutrality.

At either end of the riverfront where Leonard must have roamed were the customs houses. That at the eastern, inland end served traffic from upriver. Just beyond it was the Long Ford, where the Arno broadened and grew shallow. Men could ride their horses across in low water. Shallow-draft boats and barges floated farm produce down from the countryside, or brought merchandise from Florence and other inland towns, to serve a colorful market open in all seasons. In tents and improvised huts on the river bank and the sandy islets, foreign merchants, including Turks, Arabs, and Libyans, displayed silks, carpets, vases, and other wares.

At the opposite end of town a second customs house served vessels arriving from overseas. Near it lay what must have been one of the favorite haunts of schoolboys —the shipyard. The shipbuilding business was boom-

ing. Timber felled in the wooded uplands was barged
here, where giant cranes unloaded the huge logs. A fir
trunk destined for a mainmast might be sixty feet or
more in length. The master shipwright oversaw the
unloading, inspecting the timber minutely for defects
before accepting it. Under his watchful eye all the
varied activities of the shipyard went on at once.

Here two men operated a pit saw, one standing on
the ground above, the other down in the pit. Pushing
and hauling the huge vertical blade, they sliced through
a log shoved lengthwise against it. Nearby, men shaped
timbers with heavy hammerlike adzes with curving iron
blades. Using such crude implements, skilled workers
achieved remarkable precision in fashioning the U-
shaped frames, or ribs.

At the water's edge the frames were fixed to a heavy
keel to form the skeleton of a ship's hull, the longest
frame amidships, the shortest the tail frames at either
end. Planks were nailed to the ribs, edge to edge, to
form the sides of the ship. If this sounds like a normal
way to build a ship, it should be observed that many
great seafarers of the Middle Ages, including the Scan-
dinavians and the Arabs of East Africa, could not cut
planks accurately enough to fit them edge to edge, and
built their ships by overlapping the planks. These
"clinker-built" vessels were rarely held together by iron
nails, the overlapping planks instead being sewed with
thongs stitched through boreholes.

Even an Italian ship needed much calking to make it
seaworthy. Calkers followed directly behind the car-

penters, clambering over the new ship, sealing cracks and holes with pitch. Leonard may have envied the boys who were apprenticed to the ship's carpenters and calkers. But they worked from daybreak to nightfall, six days a week, for no pay except their keep until they won the status of journeymen—skilled laborers.

The commercial boom had created a demand for ships in other places besides Italy. Pisa built vessels for southern France and North Africa as well as for herself and her Italian neighbors. The city was almost equally famous for her ironwork. Pisan ironmasters spent the winter at the iron mines on the islands of Elba and Giglio, supervising the mining and smelting of ore in furnaces at the site. The merchant bars of iron were loaded on ships and brought to Pisa, where the same ironmasters spent the summer working them into tools, weapons, and armor.

Another major Pisan industry which imported a large part of its raw material was leather. Many of the hides were brought from Muslim North Africa. Tanners plied their trade near the Piazza San Niccola, on the waterfront, or across the river in the Kinsica quarter. Their shops were not hard to locate; tanning created a strong atmosphere. Leonard could see the master tanners and their apprentices scrape skins over a section of tree trunk to remove hair and flesh, soak them in cold water and myrtle, rub and beat them, day after day, till at length, after some six months of working, the raw skins became fine leather, to be cut and sewed into hats, belts, trousers, and other garments.

During Leonard's lifetime, leather was gradually sup-
planted by wool for clothing, an aspect of the rise of
the wool industry which played a great part in the Commercial Revolution. Spinning and weaving of wool had
always been done in the Pisan countryside. Fulling—
treating the woven cloth for softness and resilience—and
dyeing were country industries at one time, and even
the sale of wool cloth took place outside the city.
But during the early years of the thirteenth century
the industry began to shift to the city, piece by piece:
first tailoring, then the sale of cloth, then finishing proc-
esses and dyeing. Spinning and weaving were the last
skills to be urbanized.

But of all the activity going on in Leonard's city,
perhaps the most interesting was the building of the
famous tower destined centuries later to be not only the
trademark of the town, but of Italy. In the northwest
corner of the city the complex of buildings belonging
to the archdiocese had been under construction for well
over a century. The cathedral was started immediately
after the great pillaging raid on Saracen Palermo in
1063, and the work had been mightily seconded by
subsequent raids. Many of the marble columns were
literally the booty of pirating expeditions. In Leonard's
boyhood the cathedral and the baptistery stood complete, though the baptistery dome would not be added
for another century.

But the bell tower, last of the trio, was only recently
begun and Leonard was able to witness the early stages
of construction. Marble blocks were barged by canal

from quarries in the mountains. Heavy carts transported the blocks to the building site, where they were given a final dressing by stonecutters, hoisted into position by cranes, and mortared into courses. The tower had risen three of its eight stories when it became apparent that the foundation was settling unevenly.

Soil mechanics was not a very advanced science in the twelfth century. Cities standing on soft ground, like Pisa, often saw buildings lean and topple. Bonnano Pisano, the engineer in charge of the bell tower, struggled to avert catastrophe. In order to bring his structure nearer the perpendicular, he made new stories slightly taller on one side, to compensate for the lean in that direction, hoping to provide a solidly horizontal base for the upper part of the structure. But the extra masonry added weight to this side, causing the foundation to sink further. Work was suspended, and though many engineers continued to tinker with the problem, it was never solved. The tower was not completed in Leonard's lifetime, and when it was at last topped out in the fourteenth century, it still leaned.

Such was the city in which Leonard Fibonacci grew up. Benjamin of Tudela commented not only on its towers and the volume of its seagoing commerce, but added: "Its citizens are brave, and they have neither king nor prince to whom they owe obedience."

III

THE EDUCATION OF
A MATHEMATICIAN

In most of Europe education was still in the hands of the Church, but in the free city republics of Italy there were public schools. They were not for everybody; the merchant class was the privileged class, and merchants' sons filled the schools. Not only commerce, but government, required educated men. Terms of public office were short, and an ever-increasing number of citizens were involved, as senators, or consuls, or on the boards which audited the accounts of outgoing podestas, or as envoys to emperor or pope, or as technical experts dealing with the thorny problems of town government. Citizens as well as businessmen had to be able to think clearly and express themselves well.

The merchant's son in the public schools of Italy studied the "seven liberal arts." These consisted of the literary trivium—grammar, rhetoric, and logic— and the scientific quadrivium—geometry, astronomy, music, and arithmetic. Instruction was mostly oral and learning by rote. The teacher recited a phrase and the students chanted it in unison. There were no desks or chairs. Students sat cross-legged on the floor, taking notes on wax tablets, writing with a bone stylus, the ancient Roman inkless pen whose smooth side served as eraser.

The grammar Leonard and his fellow students learned was Latin. Though Pisans spoke Italian in their everyday life, Latin was the international language of the educated class. Italian merchants also spoke French, Greek, and Arabic, and Leonard eventually acquired all these languages, but none were taught in school. Besides mastering Latin grammar—the basic text had to be memorized—Leonard became adept at reading and writing Latin. He undoubtedly also learned to speak Latin. A favorite exercise was to require the student to imagine himself as Cicero or Caesar at some crisis of Roman history, and deliver an extemporaneous oration. Rhetoric also included practice in letter writing, from the composition of a business letter to the proper salutation for a prince or pope. Logic taught students to reason and debate. The trivium, in short, was a practical education for a man of affairs who might grow up to be not only a merchant or banker but statesman and diplomat.

The scientific quadrivium was given less emphasis. Astronomy was a mixture of information inherited from the ancient Greeks, including both accurate observation and fanciful invention. Leonard learned that the earth was round, and that the stars produced light while the moon only reflected it. The cause of eclipses was also correctly explained. But the earth was still thought to be the stationary center of the universe, a belief that would only be upset four centuries later by another Pisan, Galileo Galilei. In Leonard's time, sun, moon, and the "five planets"—Mercury, Venus, Mars, Jupiter, and Saturn—were seen as revolving around the earth. Further, planets and stars were universally credited with influence on the affairs of men; even educated scholars and churchmen believed in astrology.

For Leonard the two most interesting subjects in the curriculum must have been geometry and arithmetic. The geometry was culled from fragments of the work of Euclid (about 300 B.C.) as given in the Latin writings of Boethius (about 500 A.D.). Propositions from Euclid's first three books were presented without systematic connection, and without demonstration. What the student learned was little more than a series of definitions. Complete translations of Euclid into Arabic done by the Muslims had recently been retranslated into Latin, but in the absence of printing this vast work was still little known or studied.

A typical geometry problem set schoolboys was this one, from the tenth-century scholar Gerbert, who later became a pope: given the dimensions of a triangular field and the amount of grazing area needed by a single sheep, calculate the number of sheep that can graze simultaneously in the field.

Arithmetic, also based primarily on the seven-century-old writings of Boethius, taught some simple number theory. A treatise entitled *Propositions for Sharpening the Wits of the Young* was still popular in twelfth-century schools, though it was some three hundred years old. Its fifty-three "propositions" ranged from problems involving progression to simple-minded riddles:

A king, recruiting his army, conscripts 1 man in the first town, 2 in the second, 4 in the third, 8 in the fourth, and so on, until he has taken men from thirty towns. How many men does he collect in all? The answer, evolved by doubling twenty-nine times, beginning with 1, and adding all the numbers, is 1,073,741,823 soldiers (a fairly staggering number in days when an army of a thousand soldiers was considered large). (In modern notation: $1 + 2 + 4 + \ldots + 2^{29} = 1,073,741,823$.)

Another problem solved in a slightly more advanced way: a ladder has 100 steps. On the first sits 1 pigeon, on the second 2, on the third 3, and so on up to the hundredth. How many pigeons in all? The solution: add the pigeons on step 1 and step 99 (100), similarly on step 2 and step 98 (100), and so on. Step 50 and step 100 have no pairs. The answer: 49 times 100, plus 50, plus 100, or 5,050 pigeons.

Another: An old man met a child. "Good day, my son," he said, "may you live as long again as you have lived, and as long again, and thrice as much as the sum of the last two, and then if God gives you one year more, you will be just a century old." How old was the boy? The answer: 100 minus 1, divided by 3, and again by 3; or 11.

One problem turns out to be insoluble: three hundred pigs are to be killed on three successive days, an uneven number on each day. But three odd numbers cannot make an even sum. "This fable is only to provoke boys," the book concludes.

The author of *Propositions for Sharpening the Wits of the Young* derived no principles from his problems. He did not even arrange them systematically. He was more of a riddler than a mathematician. Mathematics, apart from Euclid's geometry, was in a rudimentary state.

One major reason may be found in the notation—the numerals. In Italy, as throughout Western Europe, Roman numerals were universally used. The Romans had started with "stick numbers"—I, II, III, IIII, and had added a half-dozen letter symbols—V for 5, X for 10, L for 50, C for 100, D for 500, and M for 1,000. The Roman system had the advantage of simplicity. Only seven symbols had to be learned, and addition and subtraction could be done with no difficulty. An addition problem, for example:

	M	CC	XX	III		
	M	CC	XX	III		1,223
plus	M	C	X	II	plus	1,112
equals	MM	CCC	XXX	IIII		2,335.

Sometimes it was necessary to regroup the Roman symbols in the answer and convert to a higher symbol. In the above problem, the five I's would be written as V. But the operation was simple, as long as one stuck to addition and subtraction. Multiplication and division were a different matter. With numbers of any size, they were virtually impossible. But the Romans did not need their numbers for multiplication and division, because they possessed an ancient and ingenious device. This was the abacus, still in wide use in many parts of the world in our own time.

The abacus provided the basic element that was lacking in the Roman number system—place-value, that is, the assignment of a variable value to every number depending on its place in a row. When we write "222," each of the 2s means something different:

$$2 \text{ hundreds } (2 \times 10^2)$$
$$2 \text{ tens } \quad (2 \times 10^1)$$
$$\text{and } 2 \text{ units } \quad (2 \times 10^0).$$

Apart from the abacus, place-value had no part in the Roman system. Oddly enough, an earlier culture, that of the Babylonians, had employed it. So had the Mayans of North America. The Mayans were outside the European culture stream, but why the Babylonian place-value system disappeared is something of a mystery. Probably it had to do with the fact that the Babylonians based their system not on 10 but on 60, and employed only two symbols. The first symbol stood for either 1 or 60, or any power of 60; the second stood for 10. Numbers were expressed by awkward clusters of these symbols—nine of the symbols for "1" indicating a 9, two of the symbols for "10" indicating 20. Rather late in their history the Babylonians also hit on the idea of a symbol for zero, but they did not appreciate its significance, using it only as a sort of punctuation mark in their astronomical tables, rather than as a decisive reinforcement for a place-value system. Without the zero, a symbol could stand for 1 (60^0), or 60 (60^1), or 3,600 (60^2), or any other power of 60, depending on context.

The inventive Greeks went to the opposite extreme from the Babylonians, using a number system that involved twenty-seven different symbols—their entire twenty-four-letter alphabet plus three additional figures. But their elaborate notation was less practical than the Babylonians' simple one, because they failed to use place-value.

But because they possessed the abacus, the Greeks and Romans did not really need a place-value in their number systems, at least from the point of view of business arithmetic. The abacus probably grew out of a more primitive instrument, a mere board sprinkled with sand, on which tallies were marked with a finger. Someone had the bright idea of drawing lines in the sand and dividing the board into columns, one of which could be used to represent tens, another hundreds, another thousands. The addition of pebbles or bone counters and permanently drawn lines followed. The Romans refined the abacus by constructing boards marked with grooves in which the counters could be moved without danger of their sliding into the wrong column. They also developed, or possibly borrowed, a portable abacus—much like the instrument in common use today in much of Asia—a frame with wires on which beads were strung. Usually the horizontal wires were divided in the middle, with four beads on the left and one, or sometimes two, on the right. Each bead on the left side represented 1, that on the right 5. Beads on the bottom wire were units, on the second tens, on the third hundreds, on the fourth thousands. Adding and subtracting on either the grooved board or the wire frame were easy operations, requiring few "number facts."

To add 3,476 to 2,468 or, as the Romans would have written it, MMMCDLXXVI to MMCDLXVIII, on an abacus, the first number is set up on the wires by moving the necessary beads from their position at the sides of the frame to the middle:

Thousands

Hundreds

Tens

Units

ones　　　　　*fives*

Then the second number is added:

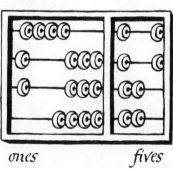

Thousands

Hundreds

Tens

Units

ones　　　　　*fives*

On the hundreds line, there are not enough counters on the left-hand side to add 4; so we add a 5 counter and subtract 1 (for which operation we must know that 5 minus 1 equals 4); in the same way, to add 2 to the thousands line, we must add a 5 and subtract 3. Then the numbers are regrouped, if necessary:

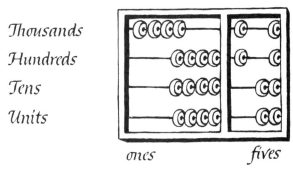

Thousands

Hundreds

Tens

Units

ones   *fives*

the two 5s on the units line going to make one 10, the two 5s on the tens line to make one 100. Then the result can be read: 5,944.

Subtraction simply reverses the process. To subtract 1,394 from 4,785, or MCCCXCIV from MMMMDCC-LXXXV, the larger number is first set up on the wires:

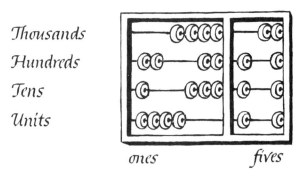

Thousands

Hundreds

Tens

Units

ones   *fives*

Then beads representing the digits of the smaller number are moved back:

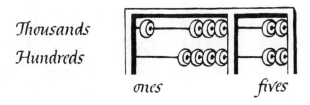

first 1 from the thousands, leaving 3; then, to subtract 3 from the hundreds, a 5 is removed and 2 added (3 plus 2 equals 5). To subtract 9 from 8 in the tens line, a bead must be borrowed from the hundreds, and the 9 subtracted from the 10 beads it represents, leaving 1 more bead to be placed on the tens line along with the 8:

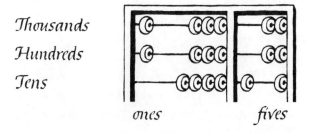

Finally, 4 is subtracted from the 5 on the units line by removing it and replacing it by a 1 (4 plus 1 equals 5):

Thousands

Hundreds

Tens

Units

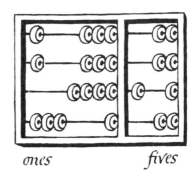

ones   *fives*

The result: 3,391.

As we have seen, a Roman or medieval merchant could add and subtract with Roman numerals, but the abacus permitted these operations to be performed with lightning rapidity. Multiplication and division, nearly impossible with Roman numerals, could also be accomplished, albeit tediously, by repeated addition and subtraction. To multiply 24 by 3, 24 was added three times; to divide it by 3, 3 was subtracted from 24 until nothing was left, with each subtraction tallied on a line of the abacus, ending with 8 tallies. It was laborious, but it could be done.

Leonard probably did not learn to operate the abacus in school. But as a merchant's son he may have become an apprentice in a *fondaco,* either his father's or that of a friend of the family. The *fondaco* was a business establishment, in the front of which customers carried on a lively discussion of merchandise, prices, and politics, while in the rear the bookkeeper kept accounts.

As an apprentice, Leonard perhaps ran errands,

learned bookkeeping, which consisted mainly of record-ing transactions in a journal, and practiced his penman-ship by copying out correspondence. Though there was no public mail service, business letters were carried everywhere by private couriers or by fellow merchants.

But the most interesting part of business life to Leonard was undoubtedly the calculating board, the abacus of the medieval merchant, arranged somewhat differently from the Roman abacus, but operating on the same principle. While the head bookkeeper added sums on the board, an older apprentice handed him counters from bowls standing next to the table while the younger ones watched and learned.

The columns on the board were usually horizontal, the bottom one representing *denarii* (pennies), the next *solidi* (shillings), the third *librae* (pounds). The mone-tary system was not decimal, and consequently the rela-tionships among some of the columns were not. Twelve *denarii* made one *solidus,* twenty *solidi* one *libra.* The fourth column up from the bottom of the calculating board represented twenty *librae,* the fifth was for hun-dreds, the sixth for thousands, the seventh and last for ten thousands.

Some bookkeepers used colored counters to indicate in-between numbers. A red counter in the *libra* column might signify five *librae.* Or a counter might be placed on the line between two columns to indicate a midway value.

For simple arithmetic, the abacus or calculating board was fairly satisfactory. Yet it had drawbacks. From a business point of view, there was the fact that the work vanished as it was performed, leaving no record. It could not be checked or corrected except by doing it over again. Already in the time of Leonard's youth, business transactions were becoming complex enough to suggest the need for a more sophisticated technique.

From the point of view of a mathematician, the combination of Roman numerals and the abacus had the same disadvantages, plus a clumsiness that made it unsuitable for anything beyond the most elementary operations. With such inflexible tools it was impossible to begin the exploration of numbers and their relationships.

A few Europeans outside of Spain were already aware of Hindu numerals, but no one realized their importance.

IV

VOYAGE TO BUGIA

While Leonard was still a schoolboy, his father was sent to Bugia (Bougie), in North Africa, to serve as a customs official. Bugia had been one of the chief cities of "Barbary"—Morocco, Algeria, and Tunisia. It was a principal source of raw materials for two of Pisa's industries, leather and furs. William Fibonacci's mission was probably to preside over the Pisan merchant community which virtually monopolized the European trade of the city, and to represent it with the Muslim authorities.

Leonard says that his father sent for him "in his boyhood [*pueritia*]," to complete his business education "with a view to future usefulness." The result must have been first of all a magnificent adventure for the boy.

Ships usually departed on a Monday in spring. On Sunday, voyagers went to church to pray for a safe journey, and enjoyed a farewell feast with their families. Early the next day they assembled at the Church of St. Paul on the Arno and mounted horses for the eight-mile journey to Porto Pisano. Pack mules carried their traveling chests. Scattered along the tree-lined road were huts of holy men, who in return for donations prayed for travelers' safety. The road traversed a swamp, and in three places required bridges mounted on pilings. The last bridge was known as the Bridge of Departure.

The Porto Pisano was crowded with ships, both sail and oared. The deep, tublike sailing ships were slow and cumbersome, but were capable of carrying the heaviest cargoes. The long galleys, independent of the wind, were swifter and more dependable, and their shallow draft permitted them to navigate river mouths. They also carried sails, a single triangular (lateen) sail on each of one, two, or occasionally three masts. A third major type of vessel, the *tarida,* was heavier and slower than the regular galley, propelled by fewer oars, but equipped with more sails on its two tall masts.

In addition to variations in capacity, maneuverability, and propulsion, the ships had other differences which helped determine their function. Galleys were cheaper to build, and could repay their cost with fewer voyages. The normal life of a ship was no more than ten or a dozen years, even barring shipwreck or capture, and in a single year only two voyages to North Africa or Spain, or a single voyage to the Levant, was possible. The stoutest of ships did not brave winter storms; late autumn to early spring was a closed season on the Mediterranean. Pisan vessels making port in Spain or Africa in the fall stayed there for the winter.

Neither sail- nor oar-propelled ships were very seaworthy in a gale. Against the other universal danger,
armed attack, the galley had a distinct advantage. Oars
were manned not by slaves but by free citizens hired
in the market place and paid wages, capable of dropping
their oars and seizing pikes and crossbows if the need
arose. The crew of a sailing ship was equally ready to
fight, but because of its smaller numbers, was less capable of defending ship and cargo.

Though Pisan ships were safe in the harbors of Muslim Spain and Africa, and immune to attack by the
vessels of Muslim states with which treaty arrangements
existed, the Mediterranean swarmed with pirates. They
were not all Muslim. Pisa itself sent out privateers,
which were built, launched, and financed exactly like
peaceful merchantmen. Theoretically they attacked only
enemy vessels, but the captain of a privateer was not
troubled by excessive scruples. People with money to
invest eagerly bid for shares in a well-known privateer.

Nearly all ships were jointly owned, often by forty
or more shareholders in complicated combinations.
Even a wealthy businessman considered it risky to own
a whole ship himself—better to divide his investment
among a dozen or more vessels.

Shipowners made their profit by charging merchants
for their cargoes and passengers for their passage. Passengers were often pilgrims bound for the Holy Land;
their fare was cheap and their accommodations poor.
They were jammed in by the hundreds below decks
and on the foredeck. The merchants, who were first-class

passengers, received different treatment. Not only were they given adequate space for themselves, their personal effects, and their servants, but they were transported free. Often even their merchandise was carried without charge when outward bound, the shipowners merely stipulating that the more expensive return cargoes from Africa or the east must travel in the same ship.

The largest ships afloat in Leonard's time were of about four-hundred-ton cargo capacity, and nearly a hundred feet long. But the typical merchantman was no more than half that size, with two decks, along the upper of which ran a four-foot solid timber barricade. At the stern rose the "castle," where the merchants were quartered. Sometimes merchants built their own temporary cabins on deck, appropriating space in proportion of the size and value of the merchandise they transported, which was itself stowed in the hold.

The ship's itinerary was fixed in advance by agreement among the merchants. Rarely did a ship sail directly from Pisa to Bugia. We may assume Leonard's voyage took him westward, with the first stop perhaps in Sardinia, which Pisans in combination with Genoese had wrested from the Muslims, and whose wealth was in its silver mines. Sardinian silver, converted into coin, now helped pay for imports from the Muslim world.

Leonard's ship probably skirted the coast of Corsica en route to Sardinia, because neither the master (*dominus*) of the ship, who represented the owners, nor the mate, who was appointed by the merchants and who was the real sailor, cared to stray unnecessarily from sight of land. After a brief halt at Sardinia, Leonard's ship probably resumed its westward course, making for either Spain or the Balearic Islands, or both, depending on the interests of the merchants on board. Malaga, on the southern coast of Spain, was frequently a port of call even if the merchants did not intend doing business there, because it served as a valuable "news stop" on conditions in Ceuta, Bugia, Mahdia, and Tunis. All four of these Muslim cities were part of the Almohad caliphate, but were dominated by different princes and factions. Pisan merchants had established formal commercial relations with them separately, sometimes by peaceful negotiation, sometimes after a fight.

Navigation in the open sea was by the stars and by dead reckoning. It is an intriguing speculation that the ship carrying Leonard may have been one of the first in the Mediterranean to employ a magnetic compass, which we know appeared in the West from China at almost exactly this time. The circular astrolabe had been known to the ancients, had disappeared in the Dark Ages, and had returned aboard ships in the tenth century. The mate measured the angle of the sun's altitude at noon, then consulted tables to ascertain how far north of the equator his vessel was.

Thus he calculated the latitude, but he had no such means for ascertaining longitude. Astronomers had worked out ways of determining it by using tables of the position of the moon, in eclipse or on the meridian, in different cities, with directions for making transpositions. But it was typical of the gap between scholars and practical men that this knowledge was used only for astrology, not for geography or for navigation. No one had troubled to do a critical study of the tables, to eliminate contradictions, and make it possible to draw a map from them.

Thus latitude could be computed with some precision, but the mariner could only estimate longitude. This was done by dead reckoning. Quitting a known coastal point, such as Sardinia, he measured his ship's speed by logging—dropping a log overboard and paying out line while keeping track of the time with a sandglass. This gave him the rate at which he was traveling, and permitted him to calculate how far he went in a day. Even an experienced navigator could make only very rough allowance for the constant alterations of wind and current, and the drift of sailing vessels at right angles to their courses.

Steering was managed by two huge oars fixed on either side of the stern—an ancient and cumbersome arrangement which nevertheless worked surprisingly well in calm weather. In the open sea the steersmen kept their eyes fixed on the North Star by night or the sun's shadows by day. When the sky was overcast they had to hope for the best and keep a sharp lookout. Few maps and charts existed, for until the use of the compass became general there was little demand for them.

In Malaga or Ceuta, and afterward in Bugia, the merchants who had chartered the ship bargained, selling their cotton and wool cloths, lacquer, iron, tin, copper, canvas, and *omnes res subtiles*—luxury goods—and buying a variety of spices, silk cloth from the East, and gold from deep in the Sahara. Gold was of especial importance, because it permitted the Pisan merchants to buy from ports in the East, the other great Mediterranean market, and chief source of the valuable spices from the Indies, much in demand among the swiftly growing wealthy class of Western Europe.

Thus commerce was a complicated affair, with many kinds of merchandise transported, and many kinds of transactions and business arrangements required. Many of the merchants who traveled on such ships as Leonard's were the "active" partners in a *commenda* or *societas*—a partnership in which a younger man took the risks of the voyage while an older, wealthier one stayed home and put up most of the capital. All these arrangements called for increasingly sophisticated bookkeeping. Italian businessmen were the most adept in Europe, but their methods lagged behind those of the Muslim merchants. Leonard's father, after spending a few years in Bugia, concluded that it was here in a major center of Muslim commerce that his son could learn the most advanced techniques.

V

BUGIA: THE ARAB WORLD

As Leonard's ship, creeping along the coast of North Africa, sighted Bugia, Leonard may have joined the other passengers in the bow to catch his first glimpse of the Muslim city. Before them, a symmetrical mountain, the Jebel Gouraya, rose almost straight out of the blue sea. At its foot, running up the mountain slope in terraces, lay the city of Bugia, the gleaming white and yellow of its houses interspersed with green palm trees and gardens. Although it bore little resemblance to Leonard's native city, it was, like Pisa, a Roman settlement—a winter resort in the last days of the empire—which had in the past century undergone a period of rapid growth and prosperity.

The ship entered the inner harbor through the massive, narrow Saracen Gate, flanked by strong forts, and joining the powerful city wall. In place of Pisa's forest of towers, Bugia's skyline was pierced by a scattering of slender minarets, which served the same function as Pisa's leaning campanile. Instead of church bells, the

minarets had muezzins, callers who from their balconies
summoned the people to prayer several times a day. The
tallest minaret rose next to the great mosque, a majestic
domed structure the equal of Pisa's proud cathedral.
Two splendid castles, the Palace of the Star and the
Palace of the Pearl, overlooked the harbor.

The walls, more than twelve feet thick, encircling
the whole city on both sea and land sides, were fortified
at intervals by asymmetrical towers which jutted out to
command fields of fire flanking all the possible approaches. A stone-arch aqueduct descended from the
mountains to supplement the water supply afforded by
the Summan, a small stream along whose banks gardens
were planted.

The waterfront of Bugia resembled Pisa's, with the
same broad-beamed sailing vessels and long, sharp-
prowed galleys crowded together. But most of the sailors
and longshoremen were Berbers or Arabs, and Arabic
dominated among the many tongues spoken. Leonard's
father probably met him at the pier and took him directly to the Pisan quarter, situated on the water front
and occupied entirely by Pisans. But Leonard was free
to enter the Arab parts of the city, where his father had
numerous connections. Bugia was a rich and cosmopolitan town, known for the elegance of its turbans and
its beribboned shoes, as well as for its candied fruits,
raisins, and wax. Bugia wax was so famous that the
town's name passed into the French language as *bougie*,
candle. Though the city had ceased to be a political
capital some time before Leonard's arrival, it was a

haven for artists and intellectuals as well as merchants and traders.

Twelfth-century Bugia was one of the many flourishing centers of the brilliant civilization of Islam. Five and a half centuries before Leonard landed at Bugia, a successful Arab businessman named Muhammad had preached a new religion in Mecca, the Red Sea terminal of the trans-Arabian trade route from India, where merchandise was offloaded from camel caravans for transshipment to Mediterranean ports. Such was the appeal of the new religion, based like Christianity and Judaism on the idea of a single God, that within a few years Mecca's foreign trade was dwarfed by pilgrim traffic. At the same time Muhammad's followers displayed a military capacity equal to their commercial talents, rapidly overrunning the entire Near East, North Africa, and Spain. The lands they conquered, stretching in a vast arc from the Caspian Sea to the Atlantic, were theoretically governed by a caliph (*khalīfah*) who was both political and spiritual leader. Two hundred years after Muhammad's death, the name of Caliph Harun al-Rashid, whose palace dominated the busy city of Baghdad, astride the trade route from the Persian Gulf via the Tigris to the Mediterranean, was a byword for fabulous wealth. His household dined from dishes of gold and silver, studded with jewels. At the wedding of his son, a thousand pearls were showered on the bride and groom, while the guests were awarded tickets with lucky numbers, each good for an estate, a slave, or other valuable. When Harun's brother Ibrahim gave a banquet, the caliph observed that the fish seemed to be cut into very small slices; he learned that he was eating fish tongues—a hundred and fifty of them.

The wealth of the caliphate came from taxes on commerce. A story told of the Caliph Omar illustrates the Muslim attitude toward business. Acting as judge in a law case Omar commanded a defendant to bring a character witness, whom Omar then interrogated: "Are you his near neighbor? Have you been his companion on a journey? Have you done business with him?" The witness explained that he knew the defendant only by seeing him in the mosque performing his religious duties. Omar dismissed the witness, saying, "You know him not," and turning to the defendant said, "Bring me a man who really knows you, for trading is the true test of a man, and it is in the operations of trade that his piety and religious worth become known."

Arab merchants ventured far and wide, bringing silk from China by caravan relays over the "Silk Road" through Turkestan to Samarkand, and reaching Morocco and Spain to the west in advance of the conquering Arab armies. They traded with the Russians of the Volga, shipping dates, sugar, steel tools, and cotton cloth across the Caspian. Handsomely figured Arab rugs and tapestries were sold in India and Europe. Paper, the secret of whose manufacture the Arabs obtained from the Chinese, was introduced by them in turn to the Europeans. In Khurasan (northern Persia) mines and quarries yielded gold, silver, mercury, and marble, all of which entered into the export trade of Islam. Intelligent

caliphs revived agriculture in the ancient Tigris-
Euphrates valleys by digging canals and irrigation works.
Harun al-Rashid even contemplated a canal across the
isthmus of Suez.

Baghdad and other Muslim commercial centers were
as noted for their culture as for their wealth. While the
rest of Europe was unaware of the writings of the
Greeks, scholars under the Abbasid (Persian) caliphs
began the work of translating the great Greek mas-
ters into Arabic. In 830 Caliph al-Mamun founded the
House of Wisdom at Baghdad, as a center for scholars.
Special commissions were sent to Constantinople to copy
Greek manuscripts so that they could be translated into
Arabic. Sometimes Arab ambassadors wrote provisions
into peace treaties that the Byzantines should turn over
certain Greek manuscripts to the Arabs. In the ninth
century, darkest point of the Dark Ages in Europe, the
Muslim world was reading—in Arabic—Aristotle's phil-
osophic works, the astronomy of Ptolemy, Euclid's *Elements,* the medical writings of Hippocrates and Galen.
To translations, scholars added their own commentaries.

Though they all wrote in Arabic, these Muslim scholars were of diverse national origins. Hunayn ibn-Ishaq
(d. 873), the son of a Nestorian Christian druggist, translated Galen and Hippocrates and many others; seven
books of Galen's anatomy, lost in the original Greek,
were preserved to posterity only in Hunayn's translation. Al-Farabi (d. 950), a Turk, was a physician, mathematician, musicologist, and political scientist, as well

as a philosopher who wrote commentaries on Plato and Aristotle and compiled an encyclopedia of science. Al-Hazen (d. 1039), a Persian, the greatest of Arab physicists, wrote treatises on optics, correcting the theory of Euclid and Ptolemy that visual rays were emitted from the eye, and on mechanics, formulating the principle of inertia that eventually became Newton's First Law of Motion. Avicenna (d. 1037), born in Bukhara, 1,200 miles east of Baghdad, produced encyclopedic works in medicine and philosophy which won him the title of "Sheik and Prince of the Learned" and made his name a synonym for scientific knowledge throughout the West. Averroës, a contemporary of Leonard Fibonacci, and the greatest of the many scholars of Arab Spain, wrote learned works on Islamic law, astronomy, and medicine, and also exerted an influence on European Catholics, like Thomas Aquinas, by his brilliant philosophical writings. These scholars and many more, all writing in Arabic, revived Greek science and philosophy, enriching it with original contributions of their own.

Arab businessmen and scholars were great travelers, journeying not only the length of the Mediterranean but into the interior of Africa and to Russia, India, and China. Ibn-Batuta, who lived in the century after Leonard, was delighted but not surprised to meet in China a man from Ceuta, near his own birthplace of Tangier, and after conversation to discover that they had previously met in India. A few years later he was pleased to encounter the man's brother in the Sudan. Like other Muslim travelers, he was no casual tourist, but a keen observer who contributed to the science of geography. Other travelers prepared maps, geographical dictionaries, and gazettes.

The Arabs brought back more than geographical lore from their travels. They collected a wide range of scientific knowledge from many different lands. One of the most important discoveries they made was in India.

While mathematics remained in eclipse in Dark Age Europe, it flowered in India. The great Indian astronomer-mathematicians Aryabhata (d. A.D. 550), Brahmagupta (d. A.D. 660), and many others took up algebra where the Greeks had left off. Their algebra was rhetorical, that is, expressed in words rather than symbols, and often in poetical and fanciful phrases. One of Brahmagupta's problems begins:

> *Into the bright and refreshing outskirts of a forest, which were full of numerous trees with their branches bent down with the weight of flowers and fruits, trees such as jambu, lime, plantains, areca palms, jack trees, date palms, hintala, palmyra, punnags, and mangoes, a number of weary travelers entered with joy . . . Sixty-three heaps of plantain fruits were put together and combined with 7 more plantain fruits, and these were equally distributed among 23 travelers so as to have no remainder . . .*

Though they lacked algebraic symbols, the Indian mathematicians possessed something equally important. Like the Babylonians and the Mayans, they had at some point, no one knows exactly when, developed the concept of place-value. Further, unlike the Babylonians, they had an admirable set of separate number symbols for 1 to 9 (gradually evolving to resemble those we use today) with which to exploit place-value. Above all, they had a zero to keep the symbols in the correct columns, so that the symbols were not ambiguous, like the Babylonian wedge which could mean 1 or 60 or 3,600 or any other power of 60. The Hindu symbol 1 could mean only 1 (10^0); if it was followed by a zero it meant 10 (10^1), if by two zeros, 100 (10^2).

It had taken the Hindus centuries to fuse the three elements—notation, place-value, and zero—into a harmonious whole. Aryabhata gave a brief explanation of place-value, and Brahmagupta laid down rules for computing with the zero. By the seventh century of the Christian era the system was apparently well established.

According to tradition, it was about A.D. 770 when a Hindu scholar, imported to the count of al-Mansur in Baghdad, introduced the Indian numerals to Islam. Some fifty years later, under Caliph al-Mamun, the great Arab mathematician al-Khwarizmi published a treatise on arithmetic which explained the new place-value notation. His name was later corrupted into the word *algorism,* which means the practice of calculating with the Hindu numerals and the zero. The title of his other major work, *Hisab al-jabr w-al muqabalah* (*Book of Calculation of Restoration and Reduction*), furnished the word *algebra.*

An eleventh-century Persian geographer, historian,

and physicist named al-Biruni completed the exposition
of the new numeral system with a commentary on al-
Khwarizmi which he produced after traveling in India
and learning Sanskrit. Still another Persian, the greatest mathematician of them all, continued the work of
al-Khwarizmi: Omar Khayyám, better known to later
times as a poet.

In the tenth century, perhaps as a result of the infil-
tration of the Hindu numerals into Arab Spain, an
improvement was made in the abacus which made its
operation very similar to calculation with Hindu numerals. It was an improvement, however, which ex-
tended only to a small circle of scholars. Though it was
in a sense a dead end, the new abacus helped pave the
way for the introduction of the new notation.

The source of the new abacus is a matter of dispute.
The chronicler William of Malmesbury claimed that
Gerbert, who taught his pupils at the archbishop's school
in Reims how to operate it, learned about it in Spain
from an Arab teacher. After ingratiating himself with
the master's pretty daughter, William says, Gerbert got
her father drunk and made off with his prized arithmetic manual. It has been speculated that this manual
may have contained the "gobar numerals," a Spanish
version of Hindu-Arabic notation. No one knows, however, whether Gerbert got his ideas from the Arabs or
not, or that he used gobar numerals in connection with
the abacus; in his written arithmetic, he used Roman
numerals.

In any case, Gerbert was not the inventor of the new abacus, because several of his contemporaries used similar computers, some earlier than he. But Gerbert's version was so successful that for a period after his death abacists were said to "gerberize" when they performed their calculations.

One of Gerbert's disciples, Richer, described the abacus which Gerbert had a shield-maker construct for him. It was a board marked off into twenty-seven compartments, the columns grouped in threes (just as we mark off thousands with commas in writing down a long number). In each column, instead of beads or counters representing a 1 or a 5, Gerbert used horn buttons (a thousand of them, Richer tells us) on which symbols for the numbers 1 through 9 were written. We do not know what form these symbols took, nor do we know the source of the strange number-names which these symbols represented: igin (1), andras (2), ormis (3), arbas (4), quimas (5), caletis (6), zenis (7), temenias (8), celentis (9).

Whatever their form or their source, Gerbert used his counters like the Hindu numerals. Each symbol took its relative value from its position. Division and multiplication could be performed with much greater ease and precision than with the Roman abacus.

Multiplication was done as we do it today, the multiplicand and multiplier placed in columns, one under the other. His pupils had to learn the multiplication tables by heart, and which columns to put the figures in.

To multiply 4,600 by 23 (Hindu numerals are used here for the sake of clarity; the exact form of Gerbert's symbols is unknown)

| | THOUSANDS | | | UNITS | | |
	Hundreds (100,000)	Tens (10,000)	Units (1,000)	Hundreds (100)	Tens (10)	Units (1)
Multiplicand			4	6		
Partial Products			1	8		
		1	2			
		1	2			
	8					
Result	1		5	8		
Multiplier					2	3

The multiplier, 23, was placed in the lower right-hand corner, the 2 in the tens column, the 3 in the units; multiplicand at the top, the 4 in the thousands column, 6 in the hundreds, the 0s represented by empty columns. The 6 in the hundreds column was multiplied by 3, the 8 of the result placed in the hundreds column, the 1 in the thousands. The 4 in the thousands column was multiplied by 3, the 2 of the result placed in the thousands, 1 in the ten thousands. Then the 6 was multiplied by the 2 in the tens column, the 2 of the result put in the thousands column, 1 in the ten thousands. Finally the 4 in the thousands column was multiplied by the 2 in the tens column, and the result, 8, placed in the ten thousands column. The partial products were then added, the result being 105,800.

Gerbert taught two ways of doing division. The first was like our present-day method, but more laborious, since each of the digits of the divisor was treated separately, instead of proceeding with the whole divisor, as we do today. The second method, which was used until the sixteenth century, was a method of differences, in which the nearest hundred, or thousand, or ten thousand of the dividend was divided by the nearest ten, or hundred, or thousand of the divisor, and the results adjusted by the difference between the round numbers and the exact ones.

Gerbert's abacus, combining the place-value of the Roman abacus with the compactness of Hindu numerals, remained in the hands of a small circle. But meanwhile the Hindu-Arabic numerals themselves were beginning to be known to scholars. During the reigns of Alfonso VI and VII of Castile, in the twelfth century, Toledo became a center where scholars from all over Europe came to glean scientific knowledge from the Arabs. Several of them—Adelard of Bath, Gerard of Cremona, and Robert of Chester—translated al-Khwarizmi's works. Like Gerbert's innovations with the abacus, their translations did not reach beyond a small audience of learned men. Neither schoolboys nor businessmen knew anything about the new number system.

This was the situation when Leonard Fibonacci visited Bugia toward the end of the twelfth century. Leonard does not say where or under what conditions he came in contact with the Indian notation. His father may have sent him to school, or obtained a private tutor.

Or he may have learned the numerals from an Arab businessman, as did Avicenna, who was sent by his father to a grocer in Bukhara to learn the same Hindu art of reckoning. What is certain is that Leonard quickly grasped the significance of place-value. For business transactions the new notation had obvious advantages over the abacus. But, possibly to his father's chagrin, Leonard saw far more in the new symbols than their usefulness in accounting. He saw in them an invitation to mathematical adventure.

VI
THE MATHEMATICIAN

After Leonard Fibonacci left Bugia, he traveled around the Mediterranean. His journeys may have been connected with his father's business, or with his own, or with the affairs of Pisa. He stayed several years in Constantinople, and visited Egypt, Syria, Sicily, and Provence. Everywhere he talked mathematics with local scholars, exchanging information and filling the gaps in his formal education with Greek and Arabic learning.

Around the turn of the thirteenth century he set to work putting down on paper the wealth of new mathematics he had acquired. In 1202 his book was published, that is, copied by hand, in Pisa. Leonard called his monumental work *Liber abaci,* literally, *Book of the Abacus.* Its stated purpose was to introduce the Hindu-Arabic numerals and explain how they were used. He continued to add to his mathematical knowledge over the succeeding years, and in 1228 issued a revised edition. It is this edition of 1228 that has come down to us.

The *Liber abaci* actually set arithmetic free from the

abacus and let it stand on its own feet. The first seven chapters dealt with the numerals themselves, what they were and how they could be used in arithmetical operations, both with whole numbers and fractions. Then these techniques were applied to practical problems—barter, converting weights and measures, money-changing, partnerships, interest. The rest of the book was devoted to speculative mathematics—series and proportion, how to solve problems by the Arabs' Rule of False Position, the extraction of roots, and finally to geometry and algebra.

The book began:

> *The nine Indian figures are:*
> *9 8 7 6 5 4 3 2 1.*
> *With these nine figures, and with the sign 0 . . . any*
> *number may be written, as is demonstrated below.*

A number, Leonard explained, was made up of units and groups of units, ascending in steps to infinity. The first of these groups was the units, from 1 to 10; then the tens, from 10 to 100; then the hundreds, the thousands, and the ten thousands, each group formed from the preceding one, starting on the right hand and proceeding to the left. If a figure in the third column to the left was 1, it denoted 100; if 2, 200; in the fourth row to the left, a figure denoted thousands, in the fifth, ten thousands. The numbers 3 and 7, written one way, made 37; if reversed, 73. A 0 indicated the absence of a number in a category: 70 was represented by a 0 in the units column, a 7 in the tens; 500 by 0s in the units and tens and a 5 in the hundreds; 290 by a 0 in the units, 9 in the tens, and 2 in the hundreds. To make large numbers easier to read, thousands could be marked off either with accents above each third number and under each fourth, or with bows over each group of threes.

In demonstration, Leonard gave several examples of Roman numerals translated into the new notation, still novel enough to him so that he occasionally lapsed into Roman numerals in his problems.

In explaining operations with the new numerals, as well as in attacking different kinds of problems, Leonard gave many illustrations to demonstrate a general method. In multiplication, he began by showing how to multiply a specific number, step by step. He supplied dozens of examples, working them all out—two-digit numbers, three-digit, four-digit, five-digit, and even eight-digit; how to multiply a number with several digits by a number with one digit, or numbers with six digits by a number with three.

He told his readers exactly how to proceed: how to write the numbers, one below the other, and the results above, being careful when performing addition to keep units under units, tens under tens, and so forth. In multiplication, he advised them to keep the partial products "in the hand"—on the fingers—or to write them down under each other and add them diagonally (as we write each partial product one space farther to

the left). Long division could be performed either as
we do it today, or by dividing the number successively
by the factors of the other number.

Square roots (treated in one of the final chapters)
were extracted according to a medieval approximation;
in modern algebraic notation,

$$\sqrt{a^2 + r} = a + \frac{r}{2a}.$$

To find the square root of 10: take the nearest perfect
square less than 10, or 9; extract its square root, 3. To
this add a fraction; the numerator will be the difference
between the original number, 10, and its nearest perfect square, 9, in this case 1; the denominator will be
twice the square root already extracted: 3 times 2, or 6.
The answer is $3\frac{1}{6}$, which, squared, is $10\frac{1}{36}$. Leonard
provided a similar approximation for finding cube roots.

For all of these operations, tables were necessary.
Above all, they were indispensable for multiplying and
dividing. A bookkeeper doing sums on a calculating
board could count the beads: 4 counters and 3 counters
made 7; with subtraction, he reversed the process. Multiplication and division were simply repeated addition
and subtraction. But to add, subtract, multiply, or
divide with the new numerals, people had to have at
their fingertips "number facts"—tables of addition, subtraction, multiplication, and division. These were included in the *Liber abaci,* along with other facts about

numbers, such as that even numbers could have odd and even factors, but that the factors of odd numbers could only be odd.

Leonard gave tables for fractions, reducing them all to "unit" fractions, with 1 as the numerator. This method went back to ancient Egypt, and perhaps derived from the fact that fractions were regarded less as numbers in their own right than as signs of division; $\frac{1}{8}$ indicated that a number was to be divided by 8; it was not a number in itself. The tables reduced $\frac{3}{8}$ to $\frac{1}{8}$ $\frac{1}{4}$ ($\frac{1}{8}$ plus $\frac{1}{4}$); $\frac{5}{6}$ to $\frac{1}{3}$ $\frac{1}{2}$; and $\frac{7}{10}$ to $\frac{1}{5}$ $\frac{1}{2}$.

Leonard preserved another ancient way with fractions—the Babylonian sexagesimals. For Leonard as for the Babylonians and the Arabs, sixtieths and powers of sixtieths were a substitute for decimal fractions. Any decimal fraction can be expressed in sexagesimals. This system has remained to this day a part of mathematical notation the world over for measurement of angles: $6°13'19''$ means 6 plus $\frac{13}{60}$ plus $\frac{19}{3,600}$ degrees.

Interestingly enough, decimal fractions, carrying place-value to the right of the decimal point, appeared in an arithmetic written by an Arab mathematician in Damascus in 952. Apparently neither he nor his contemporaries saw any great advantages in decimals, because the notation was completely forgotten for five centuries, when it reappeared in Arab mathematics. In Europe, decimal fractions were not developed until late in the sixteenth century. Medieval mathematicians also sometimes used twelfths, a basic fraction of the monetary and weights-and-measures systems. Leonard typically expressed results of money problems in twentieths and twelfths: *"librae* 4 $\frac{1}{20}$ $\frac{4}{12}$" (4 pounds, 1 *solidus,* 4 *denarii).* Practical mathematics and theory interacting, the money system may have delayed the development of decimal fractions.

Leonard wrote fractions with a bar between numerator and denominator; the appearance of this bar in the *Liber abaci* is one of the earliest examples of the device that has come down to us. Earlier, Indians and Arabs simply wrote the numerator above the denominator with no separating mark. With mixed numbers, Leonard put the fraction to the left of the whole number; instead of $5 \frac{64}{257}$, he wrote $\frac{64}{257} 5$—perhaps a vestigial survival of the Arabic right-to-left writing.

The Hindus had invented the numerals and the zero, and the Arabs had passed them on; but neither civilization had produced signs to indicate operations. Throughout the Middle Ages, mathematics struggled along without them. It remained for the Renaissance to supply plus and minus signs in the fifteenth century, the equals sign in the sixteenth. The sign for division did not appear until the seventeenth. Like the Hindus and the Arabs, Leonard wrote out his operations in words, or indicated them with diagrams. In algebra, he used the word *res* (thing) for an unknown, where x would be used in modern notations; *quadratus numerus* (square number) for x^2; and *cubus numerus* for x^3. In his *Liber quadratorum (Book of Square Numbers),* written in 1225, he also used the sign ℞ for square root. Perhaps one reason why the lack of symbols did not trouble him much was that he illustrated many of his algebraic problems with lines, or with geometric figures; thus the letter labels he gave to his lines represented the unknowns—*ab* or *gd* (the Greek origin of his algebra and geometry is evident in the sequence of the alphabet, alpha, beta, gamma, delta), or sometimes simply *a* or *b* or *g* instead of our *x* and *y* and *z*.

To check the accuracy of operations, the Hindus had invented a trick which place-value made possible, and which was used extensively by Leonard. This was casting out 9s—adding the digits of a number and striking out the 9s. To check the addition of a series of numbers, Leonard cast out the 9s in each number and in the result. After adding 4,321 and 506,789 and obtaining the answer 511,110, Leonard added the digits of the first number and struck out the 9s ($4 + 3 + 2 + 1 = 10$, cast out 9, leaving a remainder of 1); the same was done with the digits of the second number ($5 + 0 + 6 + 7 + 8$, casting out the $9 = 26$, and $2 + 6 = 8$). The sum of the two remainders was 9 ($1 + 8$), which was also cast out. Then the digits of the result were added ($5 + 1 + 1 + 1 + 1 + 0 = 9$), and the 9 cast out ($0 = 0$). The sum of the remainders equaled the remainder of the sum, and the result was checked. Analogous techniques worked for subtraction, multiplication, and division.

Place-value also provided tricks for factoring numbers. If an odd number ended in 5, it was divisible by 5.

If casting out 9s produced a remainder of 0, the number was divisible by 9. If the remainder was 3 or 6, the number was divisible by 3. An even number which produced a remainder of 0 after casting out 9s was divisible by 9; if the remainder was 3 or 6, it was divisible by 6, and so on.

The practical problems in the *Liber abaci,* demonstrating how the new numbers might be used in commercial life, have furnished scholars with information about medieval money, weights and measures, business practices, and merchandise. They indicate, for example, the importance of pepper in the merchandise that was carried on Pisan ships, signalized by the fact that at Alexandria the "pepper basket," 100 *rotuli,* was a standard unit by which other merchandise was measured. Principal kinds of merchandise were given, too: spices (saffron, ginger, cinnamon, as well as pepper); linen, wool, cotton; precious stones; skins. Other problems give some notion of current commodity prices and freight costs.

In one of Leonard's problems, two men contracted a form of partnership known as the *societas maris* ("sea partnership") at Constantinople, one man going to Alexandria to trade. From this scholars have gleaned the fact that the Pisan colony at Constantinople carried on a considerable commerce with Egypt. Another partnership problem given by Leonard explained that the first partner in a *societas* "according to Pisan custom" received a fourth part of the profit; this partner was the *tractator,* usually a young man just starting out as a merchant, who undertook the risks of the voyage but invested no capital. There were problems dealing with margins of profit, with prices, with barter. If a bale of a commodity could be purchased at a certain price, how much for a fraction of a bale? Or if you were exchanging linen for cotton, given certain prices, how many *rotuli* of cotton would be worth a certain number of lengths of linen?

Leonard gave examples of another common medieval problem, in an age when many cities coined their own money, that of alloying, or alligation—how much copper to be added to silver to produce money with a specified proportion of each metal per pound. He also provided comparative values of the money of different mints—Bolognese and Venetian *librae* compared to Pisan, and Pisan *denarii* compared to those of the Holy Roman Empire.

The calculation of interest was a favorite subject for problems: a man borrowed money at a certain rate of interest per month on a house, making payments every year which were discounted from the original debt, and the interest added to the amount of the loan each year.

These commercial problems, as well as the recreational problems that followed, Leonard solved by methods familiar to Brahmagupta and to the Arabs, such as the Rule of Three and the Rule of Five derived from it, and the Rule of False Position. Often he furnished diagrams to clarify the solutions, and to indicate a general method of procedure, taking the place of formulas for which he lacked algebraic notation.

The Rule of Three, sometimes called the Merchants' Rule, is like modern simple proportion, except that the first "thing" given is arbitrarily used as the divisor of the product of the other two numbers. For example, 4 lengths of cloth sell for 7 *solidi;* how much for 1 length? The first term, 4, automatically becomes the divisor, and the product of the second and third terms is divided by it. Leonard diagramed the problem:

	Solidi		Lengths
	7		4
Answer:	1¾		1

the diagonal lines indicating which numbers were to be multiplied.

The Rule of Five applied when there were five quantities involved, as in problems of barter like the question involving the exchange of linen for cotton. If 20 lengths of linen were worth 3 Pisan *librae* and 42 *rotuli* of cotton were worth 5, how many *rotuli* of cotton could be exchanged for 50 lengths of linen? Leonard diagramed this:

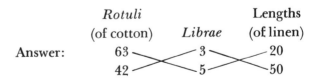

	Rotuli (of cotton)	*Librae*	Lengths (of linen)
Answer:	63	3	20
	42	5	50

Again the diagonal lines indicated the numbers to be multiplied: 50 times 3 times 42, divided by 20 times 5; result 63. In modern notation:

$$\frac{5 \cdot 20}{3 \cdot 50} = \frac{42}{x} \; ; 100x = 42 \cdot 150 \; ; x = 63.$$

Sometimes the relation of the known quantities was more complicated: "A certain king sent 30 men into his orchard to plant trees. If they could set out 1,000 trees in 9 days, in how many days would 36 men set out 4,400 trees?" Leonard wrote down the terms:

	DAYS	TREES	MEN
	9	1,000	30
Answer:	33	4,400	36

The number of trees varied directly with the number of men, the number of days varied inversely with the number of men: therefore Leonard multiplied 9 by 4,400 and by 30, and divided the result by the product of 1,000 and 36. In modern notation:

$$\frac{30 \cdot 9}{1,000} = \frac{36 \cdot x}{4,400} \; ; x = 33.$$

The Rule of False Position was another favorite technique which Leonard borrowed from the Arabs. By this method, a convenient assumption is made and a problem worked out on the false assumption, then corrected by proportion. Leonard used False Position to solve his version of the age-old problem of the Frog in the Well, which he translated into the Lion in the Pit. The pit was 50 handbreadths deep; the lion climbed $\frac{1}{7}$ handbreadth every day, and fell back $\frac{1}{9}$. How long would it take him to get out of the pit? Assuming that he got out in 63 days (since that number was divisible by both 7 and 9), Leonard calculated that he would ascend $\frac{63}{7}$ or a handbreadth in that time, or 9, and descend $\frac{63}{9}$, or 7, making 2 handbreadths' progress in 63 days. Therefore to ascend 50 handbreadths it would take:

$$\frac{2}{50} = \frac{63}{\text{number of days}} \; ;$$

25 times 63 equals 1,575.

(Interestingly, the Lion in the Pit survives to the present day as a brain teaser; Leonard's answer is incorrect, because once the lion reaches the top he is out and does not fall back. At the rate of $\frac{2}{63}$ handbreadths a day, after 1,570 days he has covered $49\frac{53}{63}$ handbreadths. On the 1,571st day he climbs to $49\frac{62}{63}$ handbreadths, but by the end of the day has fallen back to $49\frac{55}{63}$ handbreadths. When he climbs $\frac{1}{7}$ or $\frac{9}{63}$ handbreadths on the 1,572d day, he is out of the pit and so does not fall back.)

Leonard employed False Position in all kinds of problems, cisterns filling and emptying with jets and outlets of different speeds (a favorite problem in Mediterranean countries, used by Greeks, Hindus, and Arabs), ants and ships meeting and overtaking each other, trees with a proportion under and over the ground, problems of money and age.

Still another method borrowed from the Arabs was to solve a problem backward: a man went into an orchard which had seven gates, and there took a certain number of apples. When he left the orchard, he gave the first guard half the apples that he had and 1 apple more. To the second he gave half his remaining apples and 1 apple more. He did the same with each of the remaining five guards and left the orchard with 1 apple. How many apples did he gather? Here Leonard started with the 1 apple that was left; before he met the last guard, he must have had 4. At the sixth gate, then, he had 10 apples; at the fifth, 22; fourth, 46; third, 94; second, 190; first, 382. In each case the number of apples before he gives the guard his share is what was left afterward, plus 1, multiplied by 2.

A game suggested by Leonard was based on place-value: a group of men are seated in a row, one of them wearing a ring on a certain joint of a certain finger of one hand. The leader counts the wearer's position in the row, doubles it, adds 5 to the product, multiplies the sum by 5, and adds 10. To this figure he adds a number indicating the particular finger, counting the little finger of the left hand as 1 and the thumb of the right hand as 10. The sum is multiplied by 10. Finally he adds a number indicating the joint of the finger on which the ring is placed, using 1 for the fingertip, 2 for the middle, 3 for the lowest part. The person who is "It," given the result, subtracts 350. The figure in the hundreds column then shows the position of the person in the row; the tens column indicates the finger; and the units the part of the finger. (In modern notation: let x equal the position in the row of the ring's wearer, y the finger on which he wears it, and z the joint. Then $10 [5 (2x + 5) + 10 + y] + z$; simplifying, $100x + 350 + 10y + z$. When 350 is subtracted, x, the man's position, will appear in the hundreds column, y, the finger, in the tens, and z, the joint, in the units.)

Leonard often gave variations of the same problem. In one case he presented, in different parts of the *Liber abaci,* two different kinds of solution to a problem:

Two birds start flying from the tops of two towers 50 feet apart, one 30 feet high, the other 40, starting at the

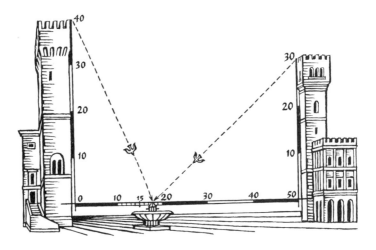

same time and flying at the same rate, and reaching the center of a fountain between the two towers at the same moment. How far is the fountain from each tower?

Early in the book Leonard solved the problem by Double False Position. Assuming that the fountain was 10 feet from the taller tower, he worked out by the Pythagorean theorem the distance that the birds would have flown, adding the squares of two sides of the triangle to obtain the square of the hypotenuse which was the flight path. But on the basis of this false assumption the two birds did not fly the same distance, the square of the distance the first bird covered being 1,700, the second 2,500.

Leonard then added 5 feet to the distance of the fountain from the taller tower, subtracting 5 feet from the distance to the shorter tower. This time the squares of the hypotenuses came out to 1,825 and 2,125.

He then calculated as follows: if the original difference in the squares of the hypotenuses was 800, and the alteration by 5 reduced it by 500, another alteration by 3 in the same direction would reduce it by 300, thereby eliminating it completely. This result could be proved: 18 feet (10 plus 5 plus 3) was the distance from the taller tower, 32 (50 minus 18) the distance from the shorter tower; the squares of the hypotenuses of both triangles were then 1,924.

Toward the end of the book he treated the same problem geometrically, reasoning from similar triangles, and arriving at the same answer.

Leonard Fibonacci's contributions to mathematics, beyond the introduction of the Hindu numerals, were mostly in the area of number theory.

Several problems in the *Liber abaci* dealt with the properties of numbers. In one, Leonard asserted that the sum of any set of numbers, beginning at 1, and ascending by 1s, or at 2 and ascending by 2s, or at 3 by 3s, would be equal to the product of the last number's rank and the sum of the first and last numbers divided by two. For example (in modern notation):

$$2 + 4 + 6 + 8 = \frac{4(8 + 2)}{2} \text{, or } 20 \text{ ;}$$

or:

$$3 + 6 + 9 + 12 + 15 = \frac{5(15 + 3)}{2} \text{, or } 45 \text{ .}$$

Applying this statement to the sum of a set beginning with 1 and ascending by 1s, Leonard produced a statement which modern students will recognize as:

$$1 + 2 + 3 + \ldots + n = \frac{n(n + 1)}{2} \text{ .}$$

Leonard used a similar device in solving a favorite problem of the Middle Ages, one of duplication (doubling)—in this case, using a chessboard, with a number assigned to each of the sixty-four squares, beginning with 1, each number double the last. Unlike the author of *Propositions for Sharpening the Wits of the Young*, who obtained the number of conscripts for his army by repeated doubling, Leonard availed himself of the fact that the sum of a series in which the number doubled each time was equal to the next number in the series minus 1 (e.g., $1 + 2 + 4 + 8 = 16 - 1$). In modern notation, Leonard's answer was $1 + 2 + 4 + \ldots + 2^{63} = 2^{64} - 1$; not content with that, he went on with the doubling process, getting a number of 39 digits.

Another kind of problem, invented by Chinese mathematicians in the first century A.D. and adopted by the Hindus and later the Arabs, was the remainder problem, which Leonard treated with many variations. In one of these, the reader was given the task of finding a number divisible by 7 which would give a remainder of 1 when divided by 2, 3, 4, 5, or 6 (the answer is 301). In another, he was to find a multiple of 7 having the remainders 1, 2, 3, 4, and 5 when divided by 2, 3, 4, 5, and 6. (The answer is 119.)

Leonard's greatest achievement in the theory of numbers, however, was in what is known as Diophantine analysis, named for Diophantus, a fourth-century algebraist of Alexandria. Diophantine algebra, a favorite with both Hindus and Arabs, is concerned with indeterminates—equations in two or more unknowns, for which a solution is required in whole numbers (integers) or common fractions (rational numbers). It is in the qualification that the answer must be in integers or rational numbers that the difficulty lies; any beginning algebra student can solve an equation with two unknowns for x, if x can be any number. But if both *x* and *y* must be integers, or rational numbers, the problem is not so easy.

Furthermore, there are two aspects of solving indeterminate equations—particular solutions, giving a number or set of numbers which satisfy each problem, and general solutions, which cover all possible particular solutions of a problem or equation. Although Leonard did not possess the algebraic symbolism to express his solutions as formulas, he did generalize, providing original thinking about numbers which was not equaled until the seventeenth century.

The *Liber abaci* contains some Diophantine problems, but Leonard's later work, the *Liber quadratorum* (*Book of Square Numbers*) is entirely devoted to indeterminate equations of the second degree (containing square numbers). The *Liber quadratorum,* a book with less immediate influence and narrower scope than the *Liber abaci,* was nevertheless an even greater masterpiece, more original and involving subtler reasoning, a systematically arranged, well-conceived collection of theorems, many of them invented by Leonard, others derived from Indian or Arabic sources, but using proofs which were the product of Leonard's own ingenuity.

A favorite Diophantine problem was finding right triangles with whole-number sides; in other words, whole-number solutions to the Pythagorean formula for the sides of a right triangle, $x^2 + y^2 = z^2$. Leonard used the fact that the sum $1 + 3 + 5 + \ldots$ of *n* consecutive numbers is n^2 ($1 + 3 + 5 = 3^2$, where 5 is the third number). Taking any odd square, such as 9, he found a second square from the sum of all the odd numbers up to but not including that odd square: $1 + 3 + 5 + 7$ (the fourth number), 4^2 or 16. Nine and 16 make 25, another square number. Similarly, the sum of all the odd numbers less than 25 is 144 (12^2, 23 being the twelfth odd number), which added to 25 makes 169, another square; and the sum of the odd numbers less than 169 is 7,056 (167 is the eighty-fourth odd number, and 7,056 is 84^2), which added to 169 makes 7,225, also a square, and so on. From these facts, he worked out a general solution to the problem, although he stated it in words rather than in algebraic formulas.

Probably his most original work was in the area of "congruent numbers"—numbers which give the same remainder when divided by a given number. (For example, 16 and 9 are congruent when divided by 7. Even numbers are congruent when divided by 2. So are odd numbers.) He worked out an original general solution for finding a number which, added to or subtracted from a square number, would leave a square number—a solution which one mathematician calls "the finest piece of reasoning in number theory of which we have any record before the time of Fermat"—a seventeenth-century genius. For centuries after Leonard's death, mathematicians borrowed from his work in this area. His statement that $x^2 + y^2$ and $x^2 - y^2$ could not both be squares was of great importance to the determination of the area of rational right triangles. Leonard left his proof incomplete; not until four centuries later did Fermat sketch a proof of the result implied by Leonard, that no right triangle with rational sides could equal a square with a rational side.

The *Liber abaci* contained a smattering of geometry to round out the wide variety of its mathematical sampling. In 1220, Leonard wrote *Practica geometriae* (*The Practice of Geometry*), containing eight chapters of theorems, mainly based on Euclid's *Elements* and *On Divisions,* which represented a considerable advance over the geometry of Boethius and Gerbert.

But the *Liber abaci,* with its elucidation of Hindu-Arabic numerals and its great range of problems, remained Leonard's best-known work. Its publication was a landmark in both the history of the Middle Ages and the history of mathematics. (For more problems from the *Liber abaci,* with solutions, see appendix I.)

VII

THE FIBONACCI SEQUENCE

A problem from chapter XII of the *Liber abaci* has made Leonard Fibonacci's name familiar to all students of mathematics, whether or not they know about Leonard's place in history:

A certain man put a pair of rabbits in a place surrounded by a wall. How many pairs of rabbits can be produced from that pair in a year if it is supposed that every month each pair begets a new pair which from the second month on becomes productive?

At the beginning, the number of living pairs is 1.

First month: 2—the first pair has produced another pair.

Second month: 3—the first pair has produced another pair.

Third month: 5—the two pairs of the first month have produced two new pairs.

Fourth month: 8—the two pairs of the first month have produced two more pairs, and the pair of the second month has produced a pair.

And so on, creating the number sequence: 1, 2, 3, 5, 8, 13, 21, 34, 55, 89, 144, 233, 377. "Thus we add the first number to the second, and the second to the third . . . and so forth . . . and thus you may proceed with an infinite number of months," Leonard concluded. At the end of twelve months, there are 377 pairs.

This sequence, presented inconspicuously in the midst of assorted problems, is the first recursive number sequence known in Europe—in other words, the first number sequence in which the relation between two or more successive terms can be expressed by a formula. Leonard's explanation shows that he recognized it as such; beyond that he seems to have attached no special significance to it. (He also omitted the first term in the sequence, as it is given today—1, 1, 2, 3, 5, 8, 13, 21 . . .)

For several hundred years neither did anyone else. In the seventeenth century, by which time algebraic notation had made progress, a mathematician produced a formula for the sequence, taking the place of Leonard's rhetorical statement: $u_{n + 2} = u_{n + 1} + u_n$ (u representing the terms, the subscript its rank in the sequence). Not until the middle of the following century did anyone notice the convergence of the sequence of ratios when one term is divided by the following one—the higher the pairs in the sequence, the closer the ratio between successive terms approaches a number between 0.6180 and 0.6181. Eighty-nine divided by 144 is 0.61805 . . . ; 144 divided by 233 is 0.61802 . . . ; 233 divided by 377 is 0.61803 . . . ; so is 377 divided by 610. At this point the ratio is established at 0.61803 . . . ; as one continues to divide terms by succeeding terms, the numbers circle around until the sixth decimal becomes established at 3 (0.618033 . . .), then the seventh at 9 (0.6180339 . . .), and so on. The ratio can also be expressed as $2:(1 + \sqrt{5})$.

At least sixteen centuries before Leonard, the ancient Greeks gave a special name to this number: the golden section. In fact, the history of the ratio goes back far beyond the Greeks. The Ahmes papyrus of Egypt (about 2000 B.C.) gives an account of the building of the Great Pyramid of Gizeh in 4700 B.C. with proportions according to a "sacred ratio." Modern measurements show that the ratio of the distance from ground center to base edge, to the slant edge of the pyramid is almost exactly 0.618. The Babylonians, at about the same period as the Ahmes papyrus was written, attributed special properties to the ratio, and so did the Greek followers of Pythagoras, who formed a secret brotherhood in southern Italy in the sixth century B.C.; both adopted as a mystic symbol the star pentagram—our familiar five-pointed star—formed by the diagonals of a regular pentagon, and made up of five lines, each of which divides two other lines in the golden ratio.

The golden ratio has also been called the "extreme-and-mean ratio," because, as in the star pentagram, it is the ratio obtained when a line is divided in such a way that the smaller part is to the greater as the greater is to the whole. This condition applies to the Fibonacci sequence, since 34 is to 55 (approximately) as 55 is to 89 (34 plus 55). In fact, architects often approximate the ratio as ⅝ (0.625)—5 and 8 being two numbers in the Fibonacci sequence.

Just as the ancients found magic in the golden ratio, they seem to have found pleasure in the proportions derived from it. Scholars have found the golden proportion or the Fibonacci numbers in the dimensions of sculpture and architecture from Greek times to the Middle Ages—in the sculpture of Phidias, in the dimensions of the Parthenon and other Greek buildings, in the great medieval abbey church at Cluny, built in the 1180s, in the dimensions of the twelfth-century Chartres cathedral.

Whether these ancient and medieval architects consciously used the golden ratio or not is a matter of debate. One writer on architecture notes that Hugh Libergier, one of the architects of Reims Cathedral, was represented on his tomb with a proportional compass which seemed to be based on the golden ratio. Although they were unaware of the Fibonacci numbers and their connection with the ratio, artists and architects of the Renaissance—among them Leonardo da Vinci—were familiar with it and consciously employed it. The Italian mathematician Luca Pacioli, late in the fifteenth century, wrote a treatise recommending the "divine proportion"—his name for the golden ratio. A century and a half later Johannes Kepler wrote about the "divine section," which symbolized God's creating "like from like."

In the 1870s a French mathematician, Edouard Lucas, coined the name "Fibonacci sequence." Lucas's analysis

revived interest in Leonard's numbers. At the turn of the century, an Oxford University botanist, A. H. Church, made a surprising discovery. Counting the spirals in the seed pattern of sunflower heads, he found numbers corresponding to those given by Leonard in his rabbit problem. On some heads 89 short spirals crisscrossed 55 longer spirals; on others 34 long crossed 55 short; on still others the numbers were 21 and 34, or 13 and 21. Since Church's discovery, botanists have found Fibonacci numbers elsewhere in nature, in the arrangement of leaf buds on a stem, of scales on a pine cone, of daisy florets.

In the 1920s Professor Jay Hambidge of Yale University invented a name for proportions based on irrational numbers, such as the golden proportion: "dynamic symmetry"—the symmetry of growth, as opposed to static symmetry, in which areas are divided into halves, quarters, thirds. This symmetry of growth was epitomized by the logarithmic (equiangular) spiral, found in snail shells and in some animal horns, and by the "golden rectangle," in which the sides were in the proportion of $2:(1 + \sqrt{5})$, or approximately 0.618. (See appendix II.) Professor Hambidge persuaded several contemporary artists to incorporate "dynamic symmetry" into their pictures.

Since the time of Professors Church and Hambidge, many people have become interested in the Fibonacci numbers. A group of mathematicians with headquarters in California joined in 1963 to form a Fibonacci

Society "to exchange ideas and stimulate research in the Fibonacci numbers and related topics." Contributors to the quarterly founded by the society have found Fibonacci sequences in the genealogical tree of the male bee, in the pine cones of the High Sierra, and in even more unexpected places. A German scientist wrote that he could recognize the golden ratio in the structure of atomic nuclei and other "fundamental asymmetries" in basic particles of matter. Some of the society's enthusiastic researchers even professed to find Fibonacci numbers in business cycles, rainfall, and commodity prices.

Fibonacci addicts have analyzed, classified, and factored the numbers in the sequence, labeling the numbers F_1 (1), F_2 (1), F_3 (2), F_4 (3), F_5 (5), F_6 (8), F_7 (13), and so forth. All Fibonacci numbers with prime labels are prime themselves (having no factor but themselves and 1: for example, F_3, F_5, and F_7 are prime numbers). All Fibonacci numbers with composite labels are composite (having at least two factors besides themselves and 1), except F_4 (3). F_6 is 8, F_8 is 21, F_9 is 34 (all composite); but F_{11} is 89 (prime), F_{13} is 233 (prime), and so forth.

Other facts that they have discovered: the sum of any ten numbers in the Fibonacci sequence is divisible by 11. Neighboring Fibonacci numbers in the series are prime to each other (have no common factors). And the sum of the numbers at any given point in the sequence is not a Fibonacci number; but if you add 1 to it, the result is the number two terms ahead. $1 + 1 + 2 + 3 + \ldots + 34 + 55$ (F_{10}) $= 143$, which is 144 (F_{12}) minus 1.

Much of the activity of the Fibonacci enthusiasts is in the realm of higher mathematics—a science that has come a long way from Leonard Fibonacci. Most of it would probably have delighted him.

But some of the speculation might have given him pause. Though he lived in an age when most scholars, however inquiring and skeptical, placed their faith in astrology and numerology, Leonard treated numbers in a purely rational way, without any of the mysticism of the Pythagoreans or of his own time. Like his seventeenth-century Pisan compatriot Galileo, Leonard was a man of science and reason.

VIII
THE EMPEROR

An indication of Leonard Fibonacci's fame in his own time is that his accomplishments as a mathematician reached the ears of another extraordinary man of science, neither merchant nor schoolman, but a prince, one of the towering figures of the Middle Ages. This was Frederick II, Holy Roman emperor and king of the Two Sicilies, whom his contemporaries called "Stupor Mundi," the wonder of the world.

Frederick was the product of the union of two remarkable families, the German Hohenstaufens and the Norman-French Hautevilles. His father was the son of the emperor Frederick Barbarossa, his mother the daughter of King Roger of Sicily, descendant of the swashbuckling Hauteville brothers, who carved their own kingdom out of Sicily and southern Italy. Frederick kept a picturesque Arabian Nights court at Palermo, enlivened by dancing girls, jugglers, musicians, eunuchs, and an exotic menagerie.

The oriental tone of Frederick's court was no accident; Sicily had long been a meeting ground for the Christian and Muslim cultures of Europe and North Africa. It had four official languages: Latin, Greek, Arabic, and French. Government officials included French-titled constables, justiciars, viscounts, Greek catapans (captains) and strategoi (generals), Arab cadis and emirs. Poetry and architecture mingled East and West. Most important, the rulers of Sicily shared the Muslim interest in science. Frederick's grandfather Roger had summoned to his court famous travelers from many lands, subjected them to interrogation, and, accepting only the facts on which all agreed, caused the results to be recorded on a great map, accompanied by an explanatory volume whose text was written by the Arab geographer al-Idrisi. Roger's successors, William I and II, encouraged the translation of Greek works on mathematics and astronomy, usually through the intermediary of Arabic. Ptolemy's *Almagest* and *Optics* and the works of Euclid, Aristotle, and Hero of Alexandria were translated from Arabic to Latin.

Frederick maintained and broadened his predecessors' interest in learning and their contact with Muslim culture. He explored every branch of contemporary science—astronomy, optics, geometry, alchemy, natural science, algebra. He dispatched questionnaires to Muslim rulers, partly as puzzles, partly in search of information. He sent the sultan of Damascus, al-Ashraf, problems in mathematics and philosophy, to which solutions, prepared by a famous Egyptian scholar, came back in the sultan's own hand. He queried scholars in Egypt,

Syria, Iraq, Asia Minor, and Yemen on the origin of the world and the immortality of the soul.

Frederick's curiosity about natural history led him to build incubating ovens to study the development of the chick's embryo, and to seal the eyes of vultures to learn whether they found their food by sight or smell. By consulting experts on falconry, he compiled a book, *De arte venandi cum avibus (On the Art of Hunting with Birds)* which included far-ranging information on birds, their classification, habits, migration, and physiology. In contrast to the credulous princes of his day, Frederick was a confirmed skeptic, refusing to accept data he could not verify.

Frederick's court was crowded with scholars from all lands. Master Theodore, sent by the Egyptian caliph al-Kamil, cast the emperor's horoscope, wrote his letters to Arab rulers, composed a treatise on hygiene for him, and made syrups and violet sugar for the imperial household. Michael Scot was the court astrologer, as well as a philosopher, mathematician, and, according to popular belief, magician. A generation later Dante consigned Michael Scot to hell as a wizard:

> *Michele Scotto . . . che veramente*
> *Delle magiche frode seppe il gioco . . .*
>
> *Michael Scot . . . who knew how to perpetrate magical*
> *frauds . . .*

Leonard later corresponded with both Master Theodore and Michael Scot, but it was a third savant, Master John of Palermo, who framed mathematical problems for

Leonard on the occasion of his interview with the emperor Frederick.

The meeting between the emperor and the merchant's son took place in Pisa early in the 1220s. It must have been a major occasion for the whole town.

Frederick traveled with a retinue that included foot soldiers, knights, officials, pages, slaves, and often his menagerie—leopards, apes, bears, panthers, and lions, led on chains. Camels carried the supplies. Hunting dogs, hawks, peacocks, parakeets, ostriches, and even a giraffe were normally part of Frederick's train. A stately elephant might bring up the rear, carrying a wooden tower where perched crossbowmen and trumpeters. At the head of the whole procession rode the young emperor. Crowds gazed at him with more than ordinary awe. In addition to his fabulous traveling court, Frederick's scientific curiosity had won him a popular reputation for dabbling in black magic.

Leonard tells us that his appearance before the emperor took place in a *palazzo* belonging to Frederick in Pisa, and that he was invited there by Master Domenicus, a member of the emperor's entourage. Some writers have speculated that a sort of tournament took place, in which several other mathematicians participated (according to the story, they were unable to solve the problems). No evidence supports this notion, however.

Frederick was about thirty at this time, athletic-looking and of medium height, with reddish-blond hair and piercing blue eyes which are said to have made his courtiers tremble. Leonard was some twenty years older.

Aware of the emperor's interest in his work, he must have felt sufficiently at ease to concentrate on the very difficult problems he was given. Leonard described three of them in his writings—two in a short work called *Flos* (*Flower*) and one in *Liber quadratorum.*

Two of them were Diophantine indeterminates. Master John very probably got them from Arabic sources. The first problem was a familiar one, and Leonard may even have studied the methods of his Arabic predecessors with it, but his solution was original and ingenious. The problem was to find a rational number (a whole number or a common fraction) such that when 5 was added to its square the result was the square of another rational number, and when 5 was subtracted from its square the result was the square of still another rational number. Leonard used this as an introduction to *Liber quadratorum,* solving it by reasoning on general numbers. His solution is too long and complex to give here; but his answer was that the number was $3 + \frac{1}{4} + \frac{1}{6}$, or $4\frac{1}{12}$, for its square increased by 5 gives the square of $4\frac{1}{12}$, or $(4\frac{9}{12})^2$, and decreased by 5 gives the square of $2 + \frac{1}{3} + \frac{1}{4}$, or $(3\frac{1}{12})^2$.

The second problem was also of a type familiar to Arab mathematicians, a third-degree equation (containing a cube). Leonard recognized that Euclid's method of solving such equations by square roots would not work here. The solution to this particular equation involved cube roots, which Euclid was unable to extract by his ruler-and-compass methods. Therefore Leonard used approximation, a method employed by astronomers since Ptolemy for determining sexagesimal fractions. Reasoning that x must be between 1 and 2 (for if it were 1, $x^3 + 2x^2 + 10x$ would be less than 20, and if it were 2 the value would be greater than 20), he narrowed down the answer by trial and error, arriving at the result (in sexagesimals): $1°22'7''42'''33^{IV}4^{V}40^{VI}$. (Here, $22'$ is $^{22}\!/_{60}$; $7''$ is $^{7}\!/_{3,600}$; $42'''$ is $^{42}\!/_{216,000}$, and so on, each subsequent fraction being expressed as a higher power of 60.) Translated into decimal fractions, the answer is 1.3688081075, correct to nine decimal places. Though the problem itself was not new, Leonard's recognition that Euclid's method could not be used was an original contribution, and his solution was far more precise than that of his Arab contemporaries.

The third problem was the easiest, an indeterminate of the first degree (containing unknowns of the first power):

Three men owned a store of money, their shares being $\frac{1}{2}$, $\frac{1}{3}$, and $\frac{1}{6}$. But each took some money at random until none was left. Then the first man returned $\frac{1}{2}$ of what he had taken, the second $\frac{1}{3}$, the third $\frac{1}{6}$. When the money now in the pile was divided equally among the men, each possessed what he was entitled to. How much money was in the original store, and how much did each man take?

To demonstrate an exercise in rhetorical algebra, let us quote Leonard's own words describing his solution as he gave it in *Flos*. (For an algebraic solution, see appendix III.)

By way of introduction, let me point out that if you take away half of anything, you have an equal half left; similarly, if you take away a third, that third is half of the remaining two-thirds; likewise, if you take away a sixth, that sixth is a fifth of the remaining five-sixths.

Let us use the term res [thing] for the amount each man received when the pile of money was divided equally among them. Then it follows that after the three men had returned the given portions of their money, the first one had half of the money in the original store minus res. The second had a third of the original store, minus the same res. The third had a sixth of the original store, minus the same res.

Since the first man had already put back half of what he originally took, and kept one-half, the half that he kept was equal to one-half the original store minus res; in other words, the whole of the money he took from the store was equal to the store minus twice res.

Since the second man put back a third of what he had taken, and that third part was half of what he kept [half of the remaining two-thirds], which was a third part of the total store minus res, one-half plus one-sixth [or ⅔ reduced to unit fractions] of what he received equaled the third part of said store minus res. In other words, the amount the second man took was equal to the total store of money minus one and a half res.

*Since the third man put back a sixth part of what
he took, and that sixth part was a fifth of what he
had left [⅙ is a fifth of ⅚] the five-sixths he had left
was equal to a sixth part of the total money minus*
res. *In other words, the third man took a fifth of the
total store minus one and one-fifth* res.

Therefore if you add: the total store minus two res
[*the amount the first man took*] *and half the store
minus one and a half* res [*the amount the second man
took*] *and one-fifth the store minus one and one-fifth*
res [*the amount the third man took*], *the total amount,
the sum of the amounts the three men took, equals
one and seven-tenths of the total money minus four
and seven-tenths* res. *Therefore seven-tenths the total
store equals four and seven-tenths* res; *therefore, multiplying seven-tenths of the store by ten, and four and
seven-tenths* res *by ten, seven times the total store
equals forty-seven* res; *therefore if you suppose* res *to
equal seven, the total money will be forty-seven* [*the
smallest possible whole-number answer*] ... *Therefore
since the first man took the total money minus two*
res, *or forty-seven minus two* res, *or fourteen, thirty-
three will remain for what the first man received.
Since the second man took one-half the total money
minus one and one-half* res, *twenty-three and one-half,
minus ten and one-half, or thirteen, will be what the
second man received. Since the third took one-fifth
the total money minus one and one-fifth* res, *nine and
two-fifths, minus eight and two-fifths, or one, will be
what the third man received. And thirty-three of the*

first man plus thirteen of the second plus one makes forty-seven, the total store.

After his triumphant interview with the emperor, Leonard kept in touch with the imperial court. His sole surviving letter is addressed to Master Theodore, Frederick's Muslim astrologer, enclosing several indeterminate problems. *Liber quadratorum* was dedicated to Frederick, Leonard noting in his dedication that he had been told the emperor had read his book (probably the *Liber abaci*) and that its subtleties about number and geometry gave him pleasure. When he revised the *Liber abaci* in 1228, Leonard dedicated it to Michael Scot.

Leonard and his cosmopolitan patrons in Sicily represented a new tradition of scientific reasoning and questioning among men of genuine intellectual curiosity. Their association was not the least important of the momentous beginnings that the Middle Ages witnessed.

IX

LEGACY

The last known reference to Leonard Fibonacci appears in a document of 1240 issued by the commune of Pisa, granting an annual honorarium of twenty Pisan pounds plus expenses for services to the city by "the discreet and learned man, Master Leonardo." Until that time he had apparently served for some years without pay as auditor for the commune.

How long Leonard lived after this we do not know. One Pisan historian guesses that he perished in the recurrent civil strife. A happier speculation holds that Leonard ended his days peacefully, laden with years and honors. In either case, Leonard had lived through Pisa's great age. Forty-four years after we last hear of him, Pisa was disastrously defeated by Genoa in the naval Battle of Meloria. Fra Salimbene, a thirteenth-century chronicler from Parma, described the battle:

They grappled their ships together after the fashion of sea fights, and there they fought with such slaugh-

ter on either side that even the heavens seemed to weep in compassion, and many on both sides were slain, and many ships sunk. But when the Pisans seemed to have the upper hand, more Genoese came and fell upon them, wearied as they were ... At last the Pisans, finding themselves worsted, surrendered to the Genoese who slew the wounded and threw the rest into prison ...

The Genoese held their Pisan captives prisoner instead of killing them, to prevent their wives from remarrying back home, thus reducing the Pisan birth rate.

The catastrophe of Meloria was only a dramatic symptom of Pisa's decline. Pisa's powerful ally, the Hohenstaufen empire, had already succumbed to changing political fortunes. Frederick II died in 1250; one by one his sons and grandsons perished at the hands of their enemies. Ghibelline Pisa was left weakened and isolated. Factional strife inside the city aggravated her situation. Wars with other cities interrupted commerce with the Tuscan interior. Finally, the swamps through which Leonard had ridden on his way to the Porto Pisano bred malarial infection which repeatedly decimated the city.

Florence, center of a growing wool industry, forged ahead to become the leader of Tuscany. Little by little, Pisa sank to the level of a minor provincial town.

But Leonard Fibonacci's great bequest to Western European civilization, the Hindu-Arabic numerals, had a history the reverse of Pisa's. At first they encountered widespread opposition. People familiar with the Roman symbols suspected the new numbers of being easily altered by the unscrupulous. They were difficult to learn, and one had to memorize tables in order to use them. Besides, people were basically conservative and resisted a new system.

But by the fifteenth century the new numerals were displacing both the Roman numerals and the abacus in European commerce and making deep inroads into noncommercial life. Coins were struck with Hindu-Arabic numerals; the numerals made their appearance on gravestones and finally on calendars. Roman symbols slowly passed into the secondary status they have occupied ever since—useful where two kinds of numerals are needed, as in outlines, and for certain traditional and ceremonial purposes, such as cornerstones of buildings.

Mathematical application of the new numerals followed a similar path. Not until the fifteenth century, when the Hindu numerals were spread by the printing press, did an awakening begin. Hindu notation soon led European mathematicians to take up algebra, probably because of the greater ease of calculation. Leonard had already pointed the way by his use of abbreviations and letter-labeled line segments for algebraic notation. In the sixteenth century brilliant progress was made in mathematics, principally in Italy, and in the seventeenth a galaxy of geniuses opened vast new fields—Cavalieri in Italy; Fermat, Pascal, and Descartes in France; Kepler in Germany. Napier invented logarithms, a development stimulated by the familiarity everyone now had with large number calculations, thanks to place-value. These mathematicians were followed by Newton and Leibniz, who built a towering new structure—calculus —and by all the vast developments of modern mathematics, which have contributed the indispensable foundation for the development of physics, chemistry, astronomy, and engineering.

Leonard Fibonacci was very much a man of his time, but he was also a man far in advance of his time. Because the business world could make do with abacus and Roman numerals, there was no popular stampede to the new notation. Pure mathematics, which gave Leonard such pleasure, remained practically at a standstill in Europe for three hundred years after his death.

As a result, Leonard's historic contribution was largely overlooked, except among historians of mathematics. Except for a French translation of *Liber quadratorum,* his works have never been translated into a modern language. Mathematicians no longer read Latin, and Latin scholars do not study mathematics. The statue in the Giardino Scotto (named for his friend Michael Scot), the quayside street in Pisa called the Lungarno Fibonacci, and a street in Florence, the Via Fibonacci, are his only public monuments.

But a change is setting in. Two American scholars are at work on the first translation of Leonard's works into English. It will be closely studied by mathematicians. Modern historians, less preoccupied than their predecessors with wars and politics, more concerned with cultural trends and achievements, will give Leonard of Pisa his due as one of the world's great intellectual pioneers.

APPENDIX I

Problems from the Liber Abaci, *for the Reader to Solve*

(Note: In the money problems, remember the medieval money ratio—12 *denarii* equal 1 *solidus;* 20 *solidi* equal 1 *libra.*)

1. THE LION AND THE LEOPARD AND THE BEAR

A certain lion could eat a sheep in 4 hours, and a leopard could eat one in 5 hours, and a bear in 6 hours; how many hours would it take for them to devour a sheep if it were thrown in among them?

2. A VOYAGE

A certain man doing business in Lucca doubled his money there, and then spent 12 *denarii*. Thereupon, leaving, he went to Florence; there he also doubled his money, and spent 12 *denarii*. Returning to Pisa, he there doubled his money and spent 12 *denarii,* nothing remaining. How much did he have in the beginning?

3. THREE MEN, FIVE LOAVES, FIVE COINS

There were two men, of whom the first had 3 small loaves of bread and the other 2; they walked to a spring, where they sat down and ate; and a soldier joined them and shared their meal, each of the three men eating the same amount; and when all the bread was eaten, the soldier departed, leaving 5 bezants to pay for his meal. The first man accepted 3 of these bezants, since he had had 3 loaves; the other took the remaining 2 bezants for his 2 loaves. Was the division fair?

4. AN INHERITANCE

A man whose end was approaching summoned his sons and said: "Divide my money as I shall prescribe." To his eldest son, he said, "You are to have 1 bezant and a seventh of what is left." To his second son he said, "Take 2 bezants and a seventh of what remains." To the third son, "You are to take 3 bezants and a seventh of what is left." Thus he gave each son 1 bezant more than the previous son and a seventh of what remained, and to the last son all that was left. After following their father's instructions with care, the sons found that they had shared their inheritance equally. How many sons were there, and how large was the estate?

5. TWO MERCHANTS WHO OFFERED WOOL IN PAYMENT OF SHIPPING CHARGES

A certain merchant sailed on a certain ship with 13 bales of wool of equal value, a second with 17 bales of the same value. When they arrived in port, the captain asked them for the charge they had agreed upon, but they did not have the cash to pay it. The first merchant said, "Accept 1 of my bales for the price of carrying the 13 bales, and give me back the change." The captain accepted, returning 10 *solidi* for the excess of the value of the bale over the charges for carrying 13 bales. When he collected the fare of the second man, he took one bale from him and returned 3 *solidi*. How much were the bales worth, and what was the shipping charge for each bale?

6. Four Men Having Denarii

There are four men, of whom the first and the second and the third together have 27 *denarii;* the second and the third and the fourth together have 31; the third and the fourth and the first have 34; and the fourth and the first and the second have 37. How much does each have?

7. Three Men Who Found a Purse Containing Denarii

Three men having *denarii* found a purse of *denarii*. The first man said to the second, "If I take this purse, I will have twice as much as you"; the second said to the third, "If I take the purse I will have three times as much as you"; and the third said to the first, "If I take the purse, I will have four times as much as you." How much was in the purse, and how much did each one have?

8. Two Ants, One of Whom Overtakes the Other
Two ants are 100 paces apart, crawling back and forth along the same path. The first goes ⅓ pace forward a day and returns ¼ pace, the other goes forward ⅕ pace and returns ⅙ pace. How many days before the first ant overtakes the second?

9. Birds Bought According to a Given Proportion
A certain person bought sparrows 3 for a *denarius* and turtledoves 2 for a *denarius* and pigeons for 2 *denarii* apiece; and he bought 30 birds for 30 *denarii*. How many birds of each kind did he buy?

Solutions

(Sometimes Leonard gives as many as five solutions to a problem, and several variations of the problem. The solutions given here are Leonard's, followed by modern ones where necessary.)

1. The Lion and the Leopard and the Bear. In one hour the lion can eat ¼ sheep, the leopard ⅕, the bear ⅙; or $^{15}\!/_{60}$, $^{12}\!/_{60}$, and $^{10}\!/_{60}$. Therefore together they would eat $^{37}\!/_{60}$ sheep in an hour, and one sheep every $^{60}\!/_{37}$ hours, or $1^{23}\!/_{37}$ hours.

2. A Voyage. Multiply 2 times 2 times 2; the result is 8; ½ of which is 4, ½ of which is 2, ½ of which is 1. Add 4 plus 2 plus 1, the result is 7; multiply this by 12 *denarii*, which the merchant spent, and the result is 84; divide by 8 and you get 10½ *denarii*.

Algebraically: if x is the original amount, then

$$2[2(2x - 12) - 12] - 12 = 0 ;$$
$$2(4x - 24 - 12) - 12 = 0 ;$$
$$8x - 48 - 24 - 12 = 0 ;$$
$$8x = 84 ;$$
$$x = 10\tfrac{1}{2}.$$

3. **Three Men, Five Loaves, Five Coins.** Each man ate $\tfrac{5}{3}$ loaves, or $1\tfrac{2}{3}$ loaves. Three loaves, or $\tfrac{9}{3}$, belonged to the first man, and 2 loaves, or $\tfrac{6}{3}$, belonged to the second. Therefore the soldier could have taken only $\tfrac{1}{3}$ loaf from the second man, and his other $\tfrac{4}{3}$ must have come from the first. But $\tfrac{1}{3}$ is to $\tfrac{4}{3}$ as 1 is to 4; so the first man should have had 4 bezants and the second 1.

4. **An Inheritance.** The total inheritance has to be a number such that when 1 times 6 is added to it, it will be divisible by 1 plus 6, or 7; when 2 times 6 is added to it, it is divisible by 2 plus 6, or 8; when 3 times 6 is added, it is divisible by 3 plus 6, or 9, and so forth. The number is 36. $\tfrac{1}{7}$ of 36 minus $\tfrac{1}{7}$ is $^{35}\!/_{7}$; plus 1 is $^{42}\!/_{7}$, or 6; and this is the amount each son received; the total inheritance divided by the share of each son equals the number of sons, or $^{36}\!/_{6}$ equals 6.

Algebraically: let S = total inheritance; let x = amount each son received, since they all had equal shares.

Then the first son's share can be expressed:

$$x = 1 + \tfrac{1}{7}(S - 1) .$$

The second son received:

$$x = 2 + \tfrac{1}{7}(S - 2 - x).$$

Therefore:

$$1 + \tfrac{1}{7}(S - 1) = 2 + \tfrac{1}{7}(S - 2 - x);$$
$$1 + \tfrac{1}{7}S - \tfrac{1}{7} = 2 + \tfrac{1}{7}S - \tfrac{2}{7} - \tfrac{1}{7}x;$$
$$\tfrac{1}{7}x = \tfrac{6}{7};$$
$$x = 6.$$

Substituting this value of x in the first equation:

$$6 = 1 + \tfrac{1}{7}(S - 1);$$
$$6 = 1 + \tfrac{1}{7}S - \tfrac{1}{7};$$
$$\tfrac{1}{7}S = {}^{3}6\tfrac{6}{7};$$
$$S = 36.$$

Dividing S by x, we find that there were 6 sons.

5. **Two Merchants Who Offered Wool in Payment of Shipping Charges.** The difference between the second merchant's 17 bales and the first merchant's 13 is 4; the difference between the first merchant's 10 *solidi* and the second's 3 is 7. Therefore the charge for 4 bales was 7 *solidi.* Change the *solidi* to *denarii,* and you have 84; divide by the 4 bales, and the charge was 21 *denarii* per bale. Therefore the first man gave 13 times 21 for the charge for his 13 bales, or 22s. 9d., to which add the 10s. the captain returned to him, and you have the value of a single bale: 32s. 9d. If you take the charge for the second man's 17 bales, 21 times 17, or 29s. 9d., and add the 3s. the captain returned to him, the value of the bale also proves to be 32s. 9d.

6. **Four Men Having Denarii.** Each man's money appears three times in the four sums; therefore if you add the sums, 27 plus 31 plus 34 plus 37, the result, 129, will be triple the sum of the four, which will therefore be 43. Subtract from this the sum of the second and third and fourth men, 31, and the result is 12, the amount of the first man. In the same way, the amounts of the other three can be found—9 for the second, 6 the third, 16 the fourth. 12 plus 9 plus 6 plus 16 equals 43.

7. **Three Men Who Found a Purse Containing Denarii.** The problem is indeterminate. One of Leonard's solutions: the second man has ½ the money of the first plus the purse, the third man ⅓ that of the second plus the purse, the first ¼ that of the third and the purse. Multiply the denominators of these fractions: result, 24. Take ¼ of 24, or 6; add ⅓ of 6, or 2: result, 8; to that add ½ of 2, or 1, and the answer, 9, is the amount of the first man. Assume the purse to be 23 (2 times 3 times 4, minus 1). Then the second man has 9 plus 23, or 32, divided by 2: result, 16. The third has 16 plus 23, or 39, divided by 3; result, 13.

Algebraically: let x, y, and z equal the amounts of the three men; let P equal the purse. Then:

$$x + P = 2y, \quad \text{or} \quad x = 2y - P\,;$$
$$\text{and} \quad y + P = 3z, \quad \text{or} \quad y = 3z - P\,;$$
$$\text{and} \quad z + P = 4x, \quad \text{or} \quad z = 4x - P\,.$$

Substituting for y in the first equation:

$$x = 2(3z - P) - P\,.$$

Substituting for z in the above equation:

$$x = 2[3(4x - P) - P] - P ;$$
$$= 2(12x - 3P - P) - P ;$$
$$= 24x - 6P - 2P - P ;$$
$$-23x = -9P .$$

At this point, to solve for x, assume a value for P that will give a whole-number answer; the lowest is 23. Then x will equal 9; substituting these two values in the third of the three original equations, we find that $z = 36 - 23$, or 13, and y then equals $39 - 23$, or 16.

8. Two Ants, One of Whom Overtakes the Other. Suppose in 60 days the first ant goes ⅓ of 60 paces, or 20, and returns ¼ of 60, or 15; thus in 60 days he would advance 5 paces. The other ant would go forward ⅕ of 60, or 12, and return ⅙ of 60, or 10; and thus progress 2 paces. Subtract 2 from 5, and 3 paces remain; and so much would they progress toward each other in 60 days. To find out how long it would take to cover 100 paces, multiply ⅓ of 60, or 20, by 100; result, 2,000 days. (Again, as in the Lion in the Pit, Leonard's answer is wrong; once one ant has overtaken the other [on the 1,999th day], the problem is ended.)

9. Birds Bought According to a Given Proportion. There are 30 birds; suppose they are all sparrows, then they would cost 10 *denarii*. But we would have 20d. left; so we must change some of the sparrows into turtledoves and pigeons. If you change one sparrow into a

turtledove, it costs ⅙ *denarius* more (½ is ⅙ more than ⅓). If you change one sparrow into a pigeon, you use 1⅔ *denarii* more, or ¹⁰⁄₆. (Here, 2 is 1⅔ more than ⅓.) Now take the 20 *denarii* left over and multiply it by 6, turning it into sixths. Result: ¹²⁰⁄₆. These 120 sixths have to be divided in such a way that one part can be divided by ¹⁰⁄₆ and give a whole-number answer, and the other part similarly by ⅙, and the sum of the two results has to be less than 30. ¹¹⁰⁄₆ divided by ¹⁰⁄₆, plus ¹⁰⁄₆ divided by ⅙, equals 21. Therefore there are 11 pigeons, 10 turtledoves, and 9 sparrows.

APPENDIX II
The Golden Rectangle

Construction of the "golden rectangle," whose sides are in the ratio of approximately 0.6180, the ratio of the Fibonacci sequence, and construction of the logarithmic spiral:

Draw a square with 2 units on a side:

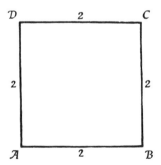

Next, draw a straight line between the midpoint of one side and one of the opposite vertices:

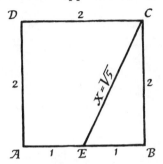

By the Pythagorean theorem, in the right-angle triangle EBC, $x^2 = 1^2 + 2^2$; or $x^2 = 5$, and $x = \sqrt{5}$, or approximately 2.236 ($\sqrt{5}$ is irrational, and the decimal fraction continues endlessly).

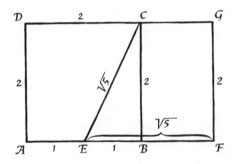

Extend the line AB to F, laying off EF equal to EC, in other words, $\sqrt{5}$, or 2.236. The proportions of the sides of the rectangle $AFGD$ are 2:(1 + $\sqrt{5}$), or 2:(1 + 2.236); therefore 2:3.236, or 0.618.

Still another geometric figure demonstrates the golden ratio, the logarithmic spiral—the only spiral that does not change shape as it grows in size. A simple way to construct such a spiral with the figure above:

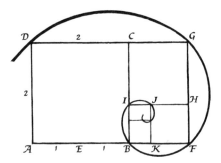

The smaller rectangle created by the construction, *BFGC*, is also a golden rectangle; one side is 2, the other $\sqrt{5} - 1$; and $2:(\sqrt{5} - 1)$ is the inverse of $2:(1 + \sqrt{5})$. Now construct another golden rectangle, *BFHI*, by dividing the smaller rectangle into a square and a rectangle; *BFHI* can in the same way be divided into a square and another golden rectangle *BKJI*, and so on to infinity. Similarly, a large square can be built on *DG* as a side, which with the original golden rectangle makes a larger golden rectangle; and so on. A spiral which runs through corresponding points on each golden rectangle is a logarithmic spiral.

APPENDIX III

Solution of the Problem on Pp. 92–95
Expressed in Algebraic Notation

Let $t =$ the total money in the store; let $u =$ the amount each man received when the money left in the store was divided equally among them. Let x, y, and z equal the amounts the men took. Then:

$$u = \tfrac{1}{3}(\tfrac{1}{2}x + \tfrac{1}{3}y + \tfrac{1}{6}z) .$$

At the end, the first man had what he was entitled to, in other words, half the original amount, $\tfrac{1}{2}t$. Therefore, before he received u, he had $\tfrac{1}{2}t - u$. He had already put back half of what he originally took, or $\tfrac{1}{2}x$, and kept $\tfrac{1}{2}x$; so:

$$\tfrac{1}{2}x = \tfrac{1}{2}t - u ; \quad \text{or} \quad x = t - 2u .$$

Similarly, the second man ended with $\tfrac{1}{3}t$. Before he was given u, he had $\tfrac{1}{3}t - u$. He had already put back a third of what he originally took, or $\tfrac{1}{3}y$, and kept $\tfrac{2}{3}y$; so:

$$\tfrac{2}{3}y = \tfrac{1}{3}t - u \; ; \; y = \tfrac{1}{2}t - 1\tfrac{1}{2}u \; .$$

Again, the third man finished with $\tfrac{1}{6}t$. Before he received u, he had $\tfrac{1}{6}t - u$. He had already returned a sixth of what he first took, or $\tfrac{1}{6}z$, and kept $\tfrac{5}{6}z$; so:

$$\tfrac{5}{6}z = \tfrac{1}{6}t - u \; ; \; z = \tfrac{1}{5}t - 1\tfrac{1}{5}u \; .$$

Adding all these:

$$t = x + y + z = t - 2u + \tfrac{1}{2}t - 1\tfrac{1}{2}u + \tfrac{1}{5}t - 1\tfrac{1}{5}u \; ;$$
$$t = 1\tfrac{7}{10}t - 4\tfrac{7}{10}u \; ;$$
$$\tfrac{7}{10}t = 4\tfrac{7}{10}u \; ;$$
$$7t = 47u \; .$$

Therefore if u is 7, t is 47. Then the original amount would be 47; the first man took $x = t - 2u$, or $47 - 14$, or 33; the second took $y = \tfrac{1}{2}t - 1\tfrac{1}{2}u$, or 13; the third took $z = \tfrac{1}{5}t - 1\tfrac{1}{5}u$, or 1; and $33 + 13 + 1 = 47$.

BIBLIOGRAPHY

SUGGESTED READING

1. THE WORLD OF LEONARD FIBONACCI

Adelson, Howard L., *Medieval Commerce*. New York, 1962 (Anvil paperback).

Cipolla, Carlo M., *Money, Prices and Civilization in the Medieval World*. Princeton, N.J., 1956.

Lopez, Robert S., *The Birth of Europe*. New York, 1966.

Lopez, Robert S., and Raymond, Irving W., eds., *Medieval Trade in the Mediterranean World*. New York, 1967 (Norton paperback).

Mundy, John, and Riesenberg, Peter, *The Medieval Town*. New York, 1967 (Anvil paperback).

Reynolds, Robert L., *Europe Emerges, Transition Toward an Industrial World-Wide Society*. Madison, 1961 (University of Wisconsin paperback).

Stephenson, Carl, *Medieval History,* ed. and rev. Bruce Lyon. New York, 1962.

White, Lynn, *Medieval Technology and Social Change.* Oxford, 1963.

2. MATHEMATICS

Eves, Howard, *An Introduction to the History of Mathematics.* New York, 1953.

Hunter, J. A. H., and Madachy, Joseph S., *Mathematical Diversions.* Princeton, N.J., 1963.

Kramer, Edna E., *The Main Stream of Mathematics.* New York, 1951.

Newman, James R., ed., *The World of Mathematics,* 4 vols. New York, 1956.

Sanford, Vera, *A Short History of Mathematics.* Boston, 1930.

Sarton, George, *Introduction to the History of Science,* Vol. 2. Baltimore, 1927–1947.

ADDITIONAL SOURCES

Adelson, Howard, *Medieval Commerce.* New York, 1962.

Arnold, T., "Arab Travellers and Merchants, A.D. 1000–1500," in *Travel and Travellers of the Middle Ages,* ed. A. B. Newton. London, 1926.

Atiya, Aziz, *Crusade, Commerce and Culture.* Bloomington, Ind., 1926.

Baxter, Lucy Barnes, *The Cathedral Builders: the Story of a Great Masonic Guild.* London, 1899.

Benedict, Suzan, *A Comparative Study of the Early Treatises Introducing in Europe the Hindu Art of Reckoning.* Concord, N.H., 1916.

Benjamin of Tudela, *Itinerary*, ed. and trans. M. N. Adler. London, 1907.

Benvenuti, Gino, *Storia della repubblica di Pisa.* Pisa, 1961.

Boethius, *De institutione arithmetica.* Leipzig, 1867.

Boncompagni, Baldassarre, *Della vita e delle opere di Leonardo Pisano.* Rome, 1854.

Brigadin, Marc Antonio, *Histoire des républiques maritimes italiennes.* Paris, 1955.

Byrne, E. H., *Genoese Shipping in the Twelfth and Thirteenth Centuries.* Cambridge, 1930.

Cajori, Florian, *A History of Mathematical Notation.* La Salle, Ind., 1928–1929.

Cambridge Economic History of Europe, Vols. II and III, ed. M. M. Postan, E. E. Rich, and Edward Miller. Cambridge, 1952, 1963.

Cave, Roy C., and Coulson, Herbert H., eds., *A Source Book for Medieval Economic History.* New York, 1965.

Conant, K. J., "Medieval Academy Excavations at Cluny," *Speculum,* 1963.

Cowley, Elizabeth, "An Italian Mathematical Manuscript," *Vassar Medieval Studies,* 1923.

Cristiani, Emilio, *Nobiltà e populo nel comune di Pisa dalle origini del podestariato alla signoria dei Donoratico.* Naples, 1962.

Dantzig, Tobias, *Number, the Language of Science.* New York, 1959.

Deansley, Margaret, "Medieval Schools to c. 1300," in *Cambridge Medieval History*, Vol. V. New York, 1929.

Dedron, Pierre, and Itard, Jean, *Mathématiques et mathématiciens.* Paris, 1959.

Dickson, L., *History of the Theory of Numbers*, 3 vols. Washington, D.C., 1919–1923.

Encyclopedia of Islam. Leiden, 1954.

The Fibonacci Quarterly. February 1963–

Ganguli, S., "The Indian Origin of the Modern Place-Value Arithmetical Notation," *American Mathematical Monthly*, 1933.

Hambidge, Jay, *Dynamic Symmetry: the Greek Vase.* New Haven, Conn., and New York, 1920.

———, *Dynamic Symmetry in Composition as Used by Artists.* New York, 1933.

———, *The Elements of Dynamic Symmetry.* New York, 1926.

———, *The Parthenon and Other Greek Temples: Their Dynamic Symmetry.* New Haven, Conn., 1924.

———, *Practical Applications of Dynamic Symmetry.* New Haven, Conn., 1932.

Haskins, C. H., *Studies in the History of Medieval Science*. Cambridge, Mass., 1927.

Herlihy, David, *Pisa in the Early Renaissance: a Study of Urban Growth*. New Haven, Conn., 1958.

Heyd, W., *Histoire du commerce du Levant au moyen âge*. Leipzig, 1923.

Heywood, W., *History of Pisa*. Cambridge, 1921.

Hitti, Philip K., *History of the Arabs*. London, 1964.

Ibn Jubayr, *Travels,* trans. R. J. C. Broadhurst. London, 1952.

Jarden, Dov, *Recurring Sequences*. Jerusalem, 1958.

Juschkewitsch, A. P., *Geschichte der Mathematik im Mittelalter*. Basel, 1964.

Kantorowicz, Ernst, *Frederick the Second,* trans. E. O. Lorimer. London, 1931.

Karpinski, Louis C., "Two Twelfth Century Algorisms," *Isis,* 1921.

Kaye, G., "Indian Mathematics," *Isis,* 1919.

Lane, F. C., *Venetian Ships and Ship-Building*. Baltimore, 1934.

Leflon, J., *Gerbert, humanisme et chrétienté au Xe siècle*. Abbaye S. Wandrille, 1946.

Lewis, A. R., *Naval Power and Trade in the Mediterranean*, A.D. *500–1100*. Princeton, N.J., 1951.

Loria, G., "Leonardo Fibonacci," in *Gli scienziati italiani*. Rome, 1919.

Lupi, Clemente, "Casa Pisana," *Archivio storico italiano,* 1901, 1902, 1903.

Luzzatto, Gino, *An Economic History of Italy*, trans. Philip Jones. London, 1961.

McClenon, R. B., "Leonardo Pisano and his Liber Quadratorum," *American Mathematical Monthly*, 1919.

O'Leary, DeLacy, *Arabic Thought and Its Place in History*. London, 1922.

Pacelli, Vincenzo, "Il contenuto economico della commenda nei documenti pisani e genovesi del secolo XII," *Bolletino storico pisano*, 1937.

Pedreschi, Luigi, "Pisa, recherche di geografia urbana," *Rivista geografica italiana*, 1951.

Pirenne, Henri, "L'Instruction des marchands au moyen âge," *Annales d'histoire économique et sociale*, 1929.

Rohault de Fleury, Georges, *La Toscane au moyen âge*. Paris, 1874.

Rossi, A., "Lo sviluppo demografico di Pisa dal XII al XV secolo," *Bolletino storico pisano*, 1945–1947.

Saidan, A. S., "The Earliest Extant Arabic Arithmetic," *Isis*, 1966.

Sapori, Armando, "La cultura del mercante medievale italiano," in *Studi di storia economica*. Florence, 1947.

Scritti di Leonardo Pisano, ed. Baldassarre Boncompagni. Rome, 1854–1864.

Smith, David E., "On the Origin of Certain Typical Problems," *American Mathematical Monthly*, 1917.

Smith, David E., and Karpinski, Louis C., *The Hindu-Arabic Numerals*. Boston, 1911.

Sullivan, J. W. N., *The History of Mathematics in Europe*. New York, 1925.

Toscanelli, Nello, "Il quartiere di Kinsica e i ponti sull'Arno a Pisa," *Bolletino storico pisano*, 1935.

Vorob'ev, N., *The Fibonacci Numbers*, trans. Halina Moss. Oxford, 1961.

West, Andrew, *Alcuin and the Rise of the Christian Schools*. London, 1892.

Wright, J. K., "Notes on the Knowledge of Latitudes in the Middle Ages," *Isis*, 1923.

Zeuthen, H. G., *Die Mathematik im Altertum und im Mittelalter*. Leipzig, 1912.

Index

About the Authors

While working on their book *Life in a Medieval City*, Mr. and Mrs. Gies encountered Leonard Fibonacci and became convinced that such an important and yet little-known figure deserved to be the subject of a book. Their research on his life and times took them to Pisa and other medieval cities, as well as to libraries in many parts of this country.

Both Mr. and Mrs. Gies were born in Ann Arbor, Michigan, and graduated from the University of Michigan. They now live in Barrington, Illinois, where Mr. Gies is senior editor of the *Encyclopaedia Britannica*. In addition to *Life in a Medieval City* Mr. Gies has written a number of books on scientific and engineering accomplishments through the ages.

About the Illustrator

Enrico Arno has had a distinguished career as a children's book illustrator. He was born in Mannheim, Germany, and educated in Berlin. In 1940 he emigrated to Italy, where he worked in book publishing in Milan and later in Rome. Mr. Arno came to the United States in 1947. He and his wife live in Sea Cliff, New York.